JAMES LEE
AND THE VINEYARD NURSERY
HAMMERSMITH

JAMES LEE

from a portrait in the possession of his descendants.

JAMES LEE
and the
VINEYARD NURSERY
HAMMERSMITH

by

E. J. WILLSON

Fellow of the Library Association
Chief Assistant, Hammersmith Public Libraries

LONDON
Hammersmith Local History Group
1961

B61-22997

Text set in Monotype 11pt. Baskerville on 12pt. body

Printed by

J. W. Arrowsmith Ltd., Winterstoke Road, Bristol 3

and published by

Hammersmith Local History Group,
a body of people interested in local history
who meet at regular intervals
and correspondence for whom may be addressed to
The Hammersmith Central Library,
London, W.6

INTRODUCTION

so far as is known this is the first biography of James Lee that has been attempted since Dr. Thornton's sketch one hundred and fifty years ago. It seems proper that this should emanate from the place not where he was born, for as with so many of his profession that was Scotland, but from Hammersmith where he made his reputation and brought up his family.

To the British public today, Hammersmith, if it is known at all, would perhaps recall a good position from which to view the University Boat Race, traffic jams at its bewildering Broadway, or entertainment at its Palais de Danse and Olympia. People come to Hammersmith in large numbers, but seldom to view it for its own sake or with any thought about its past. Yet in the later eighteenth century, Hammersmith (which was then still a part of the parish of Fulham) had a reputation ringing the world from America to Australia and Russia. Curiously enough it was the very site upon which one of its present-day attractions – Olympia – is built that brought it this renown.

Today, with more than 100,000 inhabitants crowded into its $3\frac{1}{2}$ square miles and with five major roads from London running across it, the Borough of Hammersmith has little to show of its history: There is in fact less written about its past than there is about any other borough in the County of London.

In 1955 a Hammersmith Local History Group was founded and strongly supported by the Borough Council, with the object of collecting all available material for and eventually writing an up-to-date history of the area. The last and indeed the only full length history was that of Thomas Faulkner in 1839.

Miss Willson's life of James Lee is the first major result of the Group's work, although undertaken individually by the author: in it she makes use of work resulting from another recent innovation by the Borough Council, the appointment of archivists and research assistants. These have enabled research into mediaeval records to be undertaken and have thus strengthened at its weakest point the collection of local material excellently maintained and imaginatively expanded at the Borough Library, where the author is the Chief Assistant. The Local History Group only has a membership of between thirty and forty, and its efforts up to now have been directed towards making the study of the borough's development easier by publishing maps, and towards issuing any new information obtained in an occasional 8-page publication, the *Hammersmith Historical Record*. The work of the Group is necessarily slow and Miss Willson's ability to complete one important piece of research for publication so speedily is an indication of her enthusiasm and pertinacity.

Some of the interest in local history lies in its providing material to test the generalizations necessary to historians with wider fields, and in furnishing information about the earthy roots of movements of far-reaching growth and importance. The Benevolent Despots of the eighteenth century and the many off-shoots of 'the Enlightenment' that they patronized seem a long way removed from James Lee and his homely family in Hammersmith. Yet behind the scientific academies that were being founded all over Europe and behind the rivalries of ardent collectors of plants, lay the patient skill of practical men like the gardeners Miller, Lee and Aiton. Noblemen and country gentlemen vied with each other in pursuing the hobby of plant and tree collection, in finding new species and varieties and, if they could, in seeking immortality by having their names attached to some of them. Explorers took their artists and naturalists with them, so that pictures, seeds and roots of new species flowed in from Australia, Africa and South America. Botany was as much the talk and interest of high society as were classical marbles or medallions. George III could contribute articles on practical farming and Linnaeus be ennobled for his work as a university Professor of Botany.

Linnaeus at Uppsala was the most important figure in the world of botany, and it was James Lee who popularized his work in Britain. Some of the ideas on which Linnaeus's famous system of classification was based are still important today and part of Miss Willson's work deals with the letters he exchanged with Lee and the mystery surrounding Lee's own book. But many other great names of the eighteenth century cross these pages: John Hunter the surgeon, Sir Joseph Banks, Captain Cook, Catharine II of Russia, Thomas Jefferson, and Napoleon's Josephine laying out the gardens at Malmaison, will be found amongst them.

The Second Hundred Years War against France, which forms the background of so much eighteenth century British history, appears seldom in the story but it is interesting to a later generation to see Lee's partner moving freely in wartime between England and France with his precious plants. To keep the reader in touch with well-known events there are sidelights on the mutiny of *The Bounty* and on Captain Phillip's first settlement in Australia. It was in fact James Lee who raised the first seeds brought from Botany Bay in 1788. Naturally some of the highly reputed plant illustrators appear, like Henry Andrews, Redouté and Lee's own daughter Anne: they all, including Lee himself, appear to live on terms of remarkable intimacy with society women, often learned and adventurous, bound together by their common interest in plants and gardens.

Some of the great parks and gardens of the eighteenth century nobility can still be seen and admired today, landscaped with studious informality by Launcelot Brown or along the picturesque romantic lines of Sir Uvedale Price, over whose rival ideas of planning such bitter argument could arise. When the great houses themselves were rebuilt and redecorated by the Adam brothers and their gardens supplied and tended by so many Scotsmen, England's debt to her northern partner was indeed large, and to contemporaries not always a welcome one. James Lee was one of the invaders from the North but his Hammersmith Nurseries at 'the Vineyard' contributed much to the pleasure and edification of eighteenth century society. The ten editions of his 'Introduction to Botany' in the course of fifty years betoken an influence of more than temporary or local significance only. It is to be hoped that Miss Willson's portrait of James Lee and his times will win the attention of the wide fraternity of British gardeners, great and small, who do so much to make their country attractive. It may also inspire others to peep – if only in imagination – behind the bricks and mortar of our spreading cities into a different and more leisurely world, yet one full of surprises such as the transformation of Olympia into the Vineyard.

The publication of this short study of a local worthy would have been impossible without the patronage of the Borough Council of Hammersmith, and it is most pleasurable to acknowledge a new type of patron stepping into the shoes of those that would know and help James Lee. The study is the first original work on a Hammersmith topic to be published for fifty years, if not much longer than that: as a founder member of the Hammersmith Local History Group, along with the author, I feel it a great privilege to be asked to introduce the first fruits of its work to a wider public.

Hammersmith: August 1961.

P. D. WHITTING

CONTENTS

CATALOGUE

OF

Plants and Seeds,

SOLD BY

KENNEDY AND LEE,

NURSERY and SEEDSMEN,

AT THE

VINEYARD, HAMMERSMITH.

LONDON:

SOLD BY S. HOOPER, NO. 25, LUDGATE-HILL.

M,DCC,LXXIV.

Title page (4/5 original) of Kennedy and Lee's 'Catalogue', 1774
(*from the copy in Hammersmith Public Library*)

ACKNOWLEDGMENTS

FIRST, I should like to thank members of the Hammersmith Local History Group without whose encouragement and interest this book would never have been written; in particular I should like to acknowledge the help given to me by Mr. P. D. Whitting in making many valuable suggestions, for correcting my erratic punctuation and for writing the Introduction, and by Mr. P. Roos in expert advice on the technical side of book production. To Lady Wilson, great-great-granddaughter of James Lee and through her to her sister Miss M. Lee I owe a great debt for having allowed me to share in family memories and to examine for myself family treasures and for giving permission for their portrait of James Lee to be reproduced as the frontispiece. To Mr. H. S. Pocock, who is descended from Lewis Kennedy, I am no less indebted for supplying me with details of the Kennedy family. To Mr. W. T. Stearn for reading this work in manuscript and making a number of corrections and suggestions, and to Mr. J. F. M. Cannon, without whose generous help the list of plants in the Appendix would have been of little use, I am most grateful; neither of these gentlemen is responsible, however, for any botanical errors I have made. I should also like to thank Mr. R. H. Jeffers for putting me in touch with Mr. H. S. Pocock, Mr. W. N. Lawfield for help given, and Mrs. F. M. Hobson for the map.

The libraries of which I have made the most use are the Lindley Library of the Royal Horticultural Society, The British Museum, the Botany Library of the British Museum (Natural History) and the library of the Linnean Society of London. I have also used the Library at Kew, the Guildhall Library and the Entomological Library of the British Museum (Natural History) and the public libraries of Chiswick, Fulham, Kensington, Liverpool, Twickenham and Winchester, and I should like to thank the Librarians of all of these and the staff of the London County Council and Middlesex Record Offices for their help. To the local history collection at Hammersmith Public Library, as well as to the general collection in the Reference Library, my debt is obvious. I should like in particular to thank my colleagues Miss M. E. Miles, Archivist at the Library, for giving me so much help on the manorial records and Miss J. de H. Simons, who never failed to produce the material I needed from the Reference Library.

For permission to quote from the copyright material mentioned I should like to thank the following: Messrs. Bodley Head for *The*

Beautiful Lady Craven, The British Museum (Natural History) for the Dawson Turner copies of Banks's letters, Messrs. W. Collins for *Great Flower Books*, the Linnean Society of London for letters from the Lees and Linnaeus, The National Library of Wales for part of a letter from John Lloyd, Messrs. Routledge and Kegan Paul for *Blaikie's Diary*, The Royal Society for the letter from Sir Joseph Banks to Lord Sandwich, and Mr. W. Wheatley for his *History of Edward Latymer*.

E. J.W.

CHAPTER ONE

The founders of the Nursery

EACH year hundreds of thousands of people from all over the world come to Hammersmith to visit exhibitions, entertainments and conferences held at Olympia. Very few of these visitors know that Olympia stands on the site of a famous nursery garden which in its day, too, drew travellers from all over the world to see the wonders displayed by Messrs. Lee and Kennedy at the Vineyard Nursery, Hammersmith.

The firm was that which first made the fuchsia available in England and which introduced the standard rose tree and hundreds of exotic plants into cultivation here. It is mentioned by Thackeray in *Vanity Fair*[1] and in its day was regarded as second only to Kew in the variety and extent of its collections. In 1822 J. C. Loudon wrote of it as 'unquestionably the first nursery in Britain, or rather the world'[2] when surveying the nursery gardens of the time.

James Lee, one of the founders of this Nursery, was born in southern Scotland, probably in Selkirkshire, in 1715. Nothing is known of his parents, except that, according to the writer of his obituary in the *Gentleman's Magazine*[3] of 1795 they were 'respectable. . . but not in a station that allowed them to give him any farther education than is in the power of everyone to attain in that part of Britain, and which, at that period, was generally superior to what those of that rank in England can arrive at'.

He knew Latin and it is possible that he was educated at the grammar school at Selkirk which enjoyed a high reputation in the eighteenth century. Sir Walter Scott's great-grandfather, John Rutherford, was Master there about 1680 and a Robert Petrie in 1727.[4] No school records are extant for this period so that it is not possible to say whether Petrie was Lee's teacher.

James Lee had a great love of flowers and it is said gained his knowledge of English plants from studying Culpepper's 'Herbal'.[5] He was regarded by his contemporaries as an educated man 'having received a better education than gardeners usually get, he passed with the vulgar, and mankind in general, for a prodigy in knowledge.'[6] He mixed freely with the scholars and noblemen of his time who shared his interest in natural history, by whom he was highly regarded as a botanist as well as a nurseryman.

No family by the name of Lee has been traced in Selkirkshire for his time and there is no record of his birth in the registers of births and baptisms for Selkirk, Stow, Gala, Ettrick, Ashkirk or Roberton, the only districts in the county of Selkirk for which records are available for 1715.[7]

A James Lee, who was a carrier travelling to Edinburgh and back, lived in a cottage between Yair and Sunderland Hall and died in 1826; his wife Agnes died in 1815 when she was sixty-three years old. They had a son John. All three were buried in Lindean Churchyard. This James Lee might perhaps have been a nephew, or a relative, of James Lee the nurseryman.[8]

Only one other Lee is known in connection with Selkirkshire in the eighteenth century – Dr. John Lee who was born in 1779 and died Principal of Edinburgh University in 1859.[9] The early eighteenth century was a troubled time in Scotland and it is hardly surprising that records no longer exist.

The year of James Lee's birth was the year of the rising under the Old Pretender for whom Selkirk was induced by threats to provide eleven score pairs of single-soled shoes valued at 1s. 2d. a pair. It is likely that there was some sympathy for the Pretender in the district. The Union with England, against which Selkirk had voted, had taken place only some eight years before and the inhabitants of Selkirk showed little enthusiasm when volunteers were required to fight against the Pretender.[10]

It is easy to understand why a strong healthy lad who loved flowers and insects and all aspects of nature and who was something of a scholar should want to leave Scotland and make his fortune in the more peaceful and prosperous South. Craig-Brown, the historian of Selkirk and Selkirkshire, paints a sombre picture of life in the town and county in the eighteenth century.

The Ministers and Elders of the Kirk seemed to vie with the magistrates and Council of the town in narrow-mindedness and severity. Of the former, Craig-Brown says Selkirk was 'subjected to ecclesiastical domination . . . arrogant and intolerable . . . there was nothing into which ministers did not push their meddling fingers' and of the latter they made restrictive laws 'no word uttered or act done within the bounds being too trivial for their attention'. A woman called Meg Lawson was burnt as a witch at the beginning of the eighteenth century and a belief in witchcraft persisted throughout it.

The district was poor – until 1725 there was not one cart in Selkirk. There were cattle, sheep and horses but there was little agriculture and the only inland trade was in shoes; there was some weaving of linen cloth but attempts to foster the woollen trade were not yet successful.[11]

Loudon, himself a Scotsman, writing in 1822 offers what may perhaps provide a clue to the occupation of James Lee's parents. He says 'In Scotland, as in England, it may be remarked that wherever the silk, linen or cotton manufactures are carried on by manual labour the operatives are found to possess a taste for, and occupy part of their leisure time in, the culture of flowers'.[12] It is possible therefore that James Lee's parents were, like the parents of John Lee the Principal of Edinburgh University, linen weavers.

About 1732 James Lee left his home, taking with him a fine sword,[13] a Toledo blade marked with the name of Andrea Ferrara, to begin the long walk to London. At Litchfield he was taken ill with smallpox: when he recovered he continued his journey.[14] According to Dr. Thornton (who wrote a sketch of Lee's life) he came to London under the protection of Archibald Campbell, Earl of Ilay (or Islay) who became the third Duke of Argyle.[15] This Scottish nobleman had a house, Whitton Place, near Twickenham, built for him by James Gibbs in 1725. He was famous for his love of trees (Horace Walpole called him a 'tree-monger'). He planted his gardens with Cedars of Lebanon and shrubs and filled his enormous conservatory with what was regarded by some as the best collection of exotic plants in England. This conservatory was so

3

large that when a later owner of Whitton, Mr. Gostling, split the estate into two, he was able to build himself a 'very hand-some dwelling-house' on its site.[16] The gardens had been en-closed from Hounslow Heath and were surrounded on three sides by open heath land and on the east side by the Duke's own nursery, known as 'the Rabbit Warren' in which his trees were raised. In the middle of this he had a Chinese summer house and a 'horizontal wind engine' for pumping water. The gardens themselves were embellished with a great canal, fish ponds, a bowling green, an orange walk, a gothic tower and an aviary.[17]

Dr. Thornton says, not only that James Lee worked at Whitton, but that the Duke 'continued his education and gave him the free use of his library'.[18] It is unfortunate that James Lee's only son James declared that Thornton's account of his father's life contained many 'blunders and falsehoods' without saying which parts, if any, were accurate.[19]

There is, however, other evidence that Lee worked at Whit-ton. When William Aiton compiled his catalogue of the plants cultivated at the Royal Botanic Gardens at Kew, which he published as *Hortus Kewensis* in 1789, he wished to show, as far as possible, when each plant he listed was first introduced into England and he turned to James Lee for information about the trees introduced by the Duke of Argyle. Some of the plants from Whitton had been acquired by Kew on the death of the Duke in 1761.[20]

In his preface Aiton says 'Mr. James Lee, nurseryman at the vineyard Hammersmith who remembers the gardens of Archibald duke of Argyle, at Whitton, near Hounslow, culti-vated with much care and liberal expense, has furnished the Author with a list of the trees that were introduced by his Grace'.[21]

Loudon[22] tells a different story about Lee's early career although he agrees that he was later gardener to the Duke of Argyle. He says that he first worked under Miller at Chelsea. Philip Miller, the author of the *Gardener's Dictionary*, was generally regarded as the greatest gardener of his time al-though when he grew old, according to John Ellis* his

---

* John Ellis (c.1710–1776), a London merchant who imported many seeds from America, was the author of a number of books on natural history and was the first to discover the animal origin of coral.

vanity was so raised by his voluminous publications that he considered no man to know anything but himself 'though Gordon,* Aiton and Lee have been long infinitely superior to him in the nicer and more delicate parts of gardening'.[23] Miller was in charge of the Apothecaries' Garden at Chelsea from 1722 to 1769. Several gardeners who became very well known were trained by Miller, among them William Aiton of Kew and William Forsyth (whose name is remembered in the flowering shrub *Forsythia*), superintendent of the Royal Gardens at Kensington.[24] The *Gardener's Dictionary* was a standard work which went through many editions.

That Lee received his training 'in the Botanic Way' is confirmed by Banks in a letter written to George Caley in 1798. Caley, an ex-stable boy, had been placed by Banks at Kew as a gardener's labourer to learn botany. He was not satisfied with the wages of 9s. a week and wrote a complaining letter to Banks in which he contrasted his own lack of time with the greater leisure enjoyed by a James Bolton of Halifax, an ex-weaver who kept a public-house and yet who had managed to write and illustrate a book on ferns in his spare time. In the course of his reply Banks says '... I know also that altho' there did not appear to be much time for the cultivation of the mind in the school in which I placed you, it is the very school in which the elder Aiton, Lee and Mr. Dickson and several other respectable Botanists have laid the foundation of their knowledge, and acquired a far greater degree of Botanic Knowledge, than Mr. Bolton appears by his writings to possess'.[25] Aiton, as has been mentioned, was trained at Chelsea under Miller. James Dickson began his career in the gardens of the Earl Traquair; he was a nurseryman at Covent Garden and an authority on cryptogams (flowerless plants).

If Lee worked under Miller he must have left by 1736 because in that year the great Swedish botanist, Dr. Karl Linnaeus, paid his brief visit to England; he came to Chelsea to see Miller (with whom he conversed in Latin, because he knew no English), yet in 1765 James Lee himself said he had never met or even seen Linnaeus.[26]

It may have been through Miller that Lee first heard of the binomial method of naming species (by a two-word name) and of the system of dividing plants into classes, orders, genus and

* James Gordon (d.1780) Nurseryman of Mile End.

species by the number, or some obvious characteristic of the stamens and of sub-dividing according to the number of pistils in each flower – the 'sexual system' which was an important contribution of Linnaeus to the botany of that time. Philip Miller was at first opposed to this system and he adopted it reluctantly in the 1759 edition of his *Gardener's Dictionary*, having been convinced of its utility by Sir William Watson and William Hudson.[27]

Lee was to be the first to translate the works of Linnaeus into English.

James Lee is said by Loudon[28] to have been employed at Syon before going to Whitton. Until 1750 Syon was in the possession of the Dukes of Somerset; when the last Duke died his estates passed to his daughter and her husband who later became the first Duke and Duchess of Northumberland.[29]

Lewis Kennedy, James Lee's partner in the Vineyard Nursery, is a rather shadowy figure chiefly remarkable for being Lee's partner and the father of John Kennedy, who was not only to succeed to his share of the nursery but was to become well known for his descriptions of plants in works such as Andrews's *Botanist's Repository* and as adviser on gardening to the Empress Josephine of France.

Lewis Kennedy was born in 1721 – he was therefore six years younger than James Lee. He was the son of Thomas Kennedy and Amelia Gregg (or MacGregor).[30] He is said to have worked for Spencer Compton, Earl of Wilmington, and at Chiswick, possibly for Lord Burlington.[31] If he worked at Chiswick this may account for the choice of the neighbouring hamlet of Hammersmith as the place in which to set up as a nurseryman. Dr. Thornton[32] says he was already well known as a nurseryman and florist when he went into partnership with James Lee, but at that time he was only about twenty-four years of age. He married twice, firstly Margaret Garioch in 1756 and secondly Margaret Aldridge in 1773; both his marriages took place at Fulham. He had seven children including three sets of twins; John, the only child who survived to marry and have children of his own, had a twin sister Mary; both were born October 30, 1759. An elder brother Thomas had been born on February 17, 1758. The other twins were Lewis and James born May 24, 1762 and Lewis and Amelia born March 6, 1768. Mary died in March, 1761,

6

Lewis in June, 1762, the second Lewis and Amelia both in July, 1768.[33]

None of Lewis Kennedy's letters appears to have survived and visitors to the Nursery do not mention him although he was apparently regarded as the senior partner and the firm was known as 'Kennedy & Lee' until his death in 1783.

CHAPTER TWO

Early history of the Nursery

ABOUT 1745 James Lee and Lewis Kennedy became partners in a nursery garden on a plot of land known as The Vineyard, Hammersmith.

In 1705 Bowack[1] had described Hammersmith as having 'several good Houses in and about it, inhabited by Gentry and Persons of Quality and for above an hundred years past has been a summer Retreat for Nobility and Wealthy citizens . . . This Town depends much upon the Road, and has a very great Number of Alehouses and Places of Entertainment. Also Shopkeepers, and retailers of several Commodities but the greatest part of the Inhabitants are Gardeners, Watermen, Fishers and Persons that get their Bread by their Day Labour'. It was probably little changed when Kennedy and Lee began their nursery garden because, in the 1770s, George Augustus Walpoole[2] described Hammersmith in much the same way as 'a long straggling place situated on the high Western road from London. In its neighbourhood are a great number of gardens and several very handsome seats belonging to the gentry and citizens of London'. Nathaniel Spencer[3] in 1772 put it even more briefly 'a long straggling place and only noted for its number of gardens and public houses'.

The nursery ground was on this 'high Western road from London' and was no doubt one of the 'gardens' noted.

The land lay between the parish boundary of Fulham with Kensington (Hammersmith did not become a separate parish until 1834) at Counter's Bridge and the Turnpike Gate, on the north side of the great road from London to Brentford. To use the modern equivalents, this is between Addison Bridge (still the boundary between the modern boroughs of Hammersmith, Fulham and Kensington) and Blythe Road on the north side of Hammersmith Road. The Olympia building now stands on this site.

8

The fields of which The Vineyard land consisted were known as Swanleys, Anchor Field and Butterix or Butterwicks, and all had been part of property owned by John Butterwick, or Botewyk, who was one of the chief landowners in Fulham and Hammersmith in the late fourteenth century. His property passed from him to his widow and from her to their daughter Elizabeth and her husband William Roote; by the fifteenth century it was in the possession of the Essex family who kept it until 1573; after that it passed through a number of hands until in 1622 Edward Latymer purchased part of it specified as 'two messuages, three cottages, two gardens, two orchards, 80 acres of land, 10 acres of meadow, 30 acres of pasture, 16 acres of wood'.[4] This included the land which became the Vineyard Nursery and much other property besides.

Swanleys, Swan Leas, Swanne Leaze or Swanfield (different forms of name are used at various times) seems to have been the name given to a large field which was divided into the 4 acres 1 rood 2 perches which was part of the property left by Edward Latymer to the Poor of Edmonton fronting along the main road[5] and the manorial land, also '4 acres more or less' in extent, north of this and bordered on the west by Blythe Road then called Blind Lane. It was for the Kennedy half-share of this that the second James Lee was to pay £300 in 1818.[6] Edward Latymer's will of 1624 leaves to the poor of Edmonton 'one close of arrable land, meadowe or pasture lyinge and beinge near unto the towne of Hammersmith aforesaid and nowe in occupacon of Thomas Earesbrie or William Eresbrie his sonne sometimes called by the name of Swanne leaze . . . .'[7]

This land was still in the possession of the Latymer Charity of Edmonton, leased to James Lee, the younger, when the Charity Commission made its report in 1823.[8] The land James Lee, the younger, purchased in 1818 'one undivided Moiety or half part of' from John Kennedy (Lewis Kennedy's son) was described as 'All that Close of Customany Land called Swanleys containing in estimation Four acres more or less situate near Blind Lane in Hammersmith within and holden of the same Manor by the yearly Quit Rent of one shilling'.[9]

There are glimpses of the land at various earlier periods.

In 1508 the heirs of John Cokeryke were ordered to scour their ditch on the west of Swanleys or pay a penalty of 12*d*. In March, 1556, Thomas Essex was accused of allowing the hedgerows of his 'certen growndes cawlled Round Closses and Swan Leas, the which lyeth between Hammersmith and Kensington nye unto Counties Bryde', Counter's Bridge, to 'growe so thyck with under woodes, that it is a grett harbour for theeves.'[10] The Court Rolls of 1617 show William Davis ordered to 'scour his ditch from Counter's bridge to the gate of his close called Swanleys'.[11] In 1630 William Caursbee (which is probably another spelling from the Eresbrie mentioned in Latymer's will) was ordered by the Manorial Court to scour his ditch leading from Counter's Bridge to Blind lane end.[12]

Two years before, Thomas Iles had passed to John Iles property amongst which was '1 tenement called the Swanne* with three barnes, 1 stable and 2 sheds in the tenure of Michael Lawrence and Christopher Smith' and 'one other cottage called "Vynehouse", a barn and garden in tenure of Michael Lawrence'[13] while in April, 1686, another Earesby, Thomas, passed to Henry Bristowe, wine cooper, one cottage with five roods of ground lately in occupation of Thomas Exland abutting east on land of Mr. Iles and 'le swan entry' west on land of Mr. Richard Bastion and south on the King's highway. Henry Bristow surrendered this property immediately to Thomas Reynolds.[14]

In 1716 Mrs. Whichelow was paying 2*s*. to the Manor for the right of entry to Swanleys. By October, 1731, the land was in the hands of Margaret Whitchello, widow, who surrendered the property to George Whitchello of St. Margaret's, Westminster, coal merchant, conditionally. In October, 1731, she is described as Margaret Whitchells, widow, and as surrendering a close of 4 acres called Swanleys for her own use for life and then to her daughter Margaret Whitchells, spinster.[15]

The name 'Anchor Field' occurs in a land Registry Memorial of 1818 – it is described as being of two acres in extent and fronting the road and adjoining the Hammersmith Turnpike.[16] This was land by the 'Bell and Anchor' public-house which still stands on the corner of Blythe Road (although it

* There is no proof that this is identical with Swanleys.

has been rebuilt) and it is probably the name for the western part of Swanleys.

The 'Bell and Anchor' also stood on Edmonton Charity land. It was very conveniently situated just by the Turnpike Gate and in the late eighteenth century was the 'resort of fashion'.[17] It had not always been so. At the time that Kennedy and Lee opened their Nursery it was known as 'The Robin Hood' ale house kept by a John Tunks. Tunks made such a nuisance of himself obstructing and assaulting the toll-collectors at the Gate that the Trustees of the Brentford Turnpike Trust (who were responsible for the road) successfully opposed the renewal of his licence in 1754. His successor Mark Conture changed the name to 'Bell and Anchor' which it has remained ever since.[18]

Butterwick, described as 'all those closes of land, meadow and pasture containing . . . 25 acres . . called Butterix alias Butterwickes', was sold by Edward Latymer's executors in 1628 to William Chalkhill, the elder, of Starch Green.[19] This land was subsequently split up and in 1670 Sir Joseph Sheldon was in possession of 'seven closes of land called Buttericks' which consisted of eighteen acres.[20] In March 1713 Joan Jordan, widow, and Thomas Jordan of Hammersmith, gardener, and his wife Mary surrendered a parcel of 3½ acres of orchard and garden land near Blind Lane and west of Butterix to Edward Billingsly of St. Martin in the Fields, gentleman. In December 1745 Edward Billingsly, described as 'late of Ealing' surrendered this property to Edward Jug and Robert Careless upon trust to provide an annuity for a servant. This might be part of the Nursery's part of Butterwick. A survey of Hammersmith made in 1829[21] shows Messrs. Lee as owners of 'about three acres of nursery ground and a small part called Swanfield, with ten hot-houses and greenhouses', the area of which is given as three acres, three roods, fifteen perches. They were also tenants of the Latymer Charity of Edmonton for 'House, stables, sheds, greenhouse and about four acres of nursery garden ground' – the exact area is given as five acres, twenty-five perches, and tenants for an unnamed owner of 'About [nine] acres of nursery ground called Butterwick with one green house'; the area for this is given as nine acres, one rood, eight perches. The total area of the Nursery in 1829 was therefore just over eighteen acres. Nearly fifteen further acres of 'Brick Earth Land called Butterwick' are also listed as in the tenancy of Messrs. Bird and of Messrs. Scott; this accounts for most of the twenty-five acres 'called Butterix' which Edward Latymer's executors sold in 1628. It seems more likely that Edward Billingsly's 'orchard and garden' ground would have become part of the Nursery than have been used as 'Brick Earth Land'.

Before Lewis Kennedy and James Lee turned the land into a nursery garden it had been a vineyard. Who their immediate predecessors were we do not know because there is no further mention of Swanleys or Butterwick in the Court Rolls which have been searched to 1760.[22] There is a note in an unknown hand in an annotated copy of Faulkner's 'Fulham' stating that Paul Gervaise had the land before Lee and Kennedy but no confirmation of this has been discovered.[23]

The growing of vines in the open air in England was introduced by the Romans in A.D.280 and flourished for a time but a combination of a worsening of climatic conditions, making vine-growing more difficult, and the competition of cheap wines imported from France in the fourteenth century led to a gradual decline in the cultivation of vines. The dissolution of the monasteries by scattering the monks, the most skilled vine-growers remaining, gave it a further blow from which it did not recover.[24] Nevertheless, a few vineyards continued to be cultivated, among them the one at Hammersmith. The mention of a cottage called 'Vynehouse' in 1628 and of a wine cooper, Henry Bristowe, in 1686 in connection with the land seem to show that it was a vineyard then.

Dr. Hales in his *Compleat Treatise of Practical Husbandry* quoted by Vispré in 1786,[25] says 'I have drunk with the distinguished and eminent Dr. Shaw wines made under his own care from a little vineyard behind his own garden at Kensington which equal many of the lighter wines of France and while good care was taken of the vineyard at Hammersmith a great deal of very good [wine] was obtained for sale though neither of these were favourable plots'. H. M. Todd in his book *Vine growing in England*, published in 1911, says 'a considerable quantity of Burgundy wine was made year by year' at Hammersmith, 'somewhere I have read that 100 hogsheads was not unusual. Be that as it may various writers have agreed in describing the wine as good, very good and excellent'.

When Kennedy and Lee took over the land there was a thatched house in the grounds the upper part of which was used as a dwelling-house and had been used for selling the wine; there were wine cellars under it. This may be the cottage described as 'Vynehouse' in 1628. Thomas Worlidge, the engraver, lived in this house during the last years of his life.[26]

In addition to the land in what is now the borough of Hammersmith but which in Lee and Kennedy's time was known as the 'Hammersmith side' of the parish of Fulham, the nursery also had grounds on the opposite side of the main road in Fulham from 1762 when the ground was taken over from Ann Harris.[27] This is no doubt the same land as that in the parish of St. Mary, Fulham described under 'Portland Place, North End' in 1818 and under 'Behind Vale Place' in 1821 in the records of the Westminster Commissioners of Sewers,[28] which, as a map[29] in the same records shows, at that time adjoined the land of Mr. Clarke whose land had Counter's Creek as its boundary on the east.

As tenants and landowners James Lee and Lewis Kennedy were liable not only to pay various taxes but also to perform certain duties if called upon.

In March 1769 'Lewis Kennedy Nursery Man' was one of the seven Hammersmith men included in the Jury of Sewers, but his name does not appear in the list of Jurymen sworn in on July 10. The Jury had the duty of seeing that owners and occupiers of property kept their sewers, ditches and water courses in a proper state of repair and, if necessary, of levying a rate to pay for work to be done.

In August it was 'ordered that Lewis Kennedy and James Lee as to twelve rods of the course of the ancient sewer within the Hamlet of Hammersmith near the Place called Blind Lane [now Blythe Road] upon which their land doth abut towards the North do on or before the fourth day of September next ensuing Cleanse, Repair and Amend or Sustain bear and pay the Costs or Charges of Cleansing and Amending such part of the sd. Sewer before ment.[ioned] and remove the Annoyances and Impediments on such said Space or Length of the Course of the Said Sewer or Shew to this Court good Cause to the contrary and it is further ordered that William Down, Surveyor to this Court do

Inspect the Cleaning . . . and that he report whether the same have been fully or sufficiently Performed or not'.

Reports on progress made by various occupiers who had been ordered to cleanse their drainage channels were received by the Court in September. No mention was made of Kennedy and Lee but it was stated that 'several persons on whom orders were made at the last Court . . . representing that the Harvest was not compleatly finished and assigning other reasonable excuses . . . it was ordered that further time be given'. What happened next is not known. The right of the Westminster Commissioners of Sewers to extend their jurisdiction so far west as Hammersmith was challenged by Thomas Yeaw in 1770 and as the Commissioners lost their case, no further eighteenth century records exist for the Counter's Creek area of Hammersmith. There is, however, an interesting plan of the Counter's Creek Sewer for 1770. Counter's Creek formed the boundary of the parish of Fulham with Kensington and at that time also the eastern boundary of the Vineyard Nursery. The plan shows the landowners on both sides of the Creek from what is now Uxbridge Road (called 'North road to Kensington Gravel Pits', i.e., Notting Hill Gate, on the plan) to the Thames. From the 'road to Kensington', now Hammersmith Road, northwards, Messrs. Lee and Kennedy had 31 rods, Stephen Randall 51 rods and another 96 rods, 'Mr. Smith of Brook Green' 47 rods, then what is now Uxbridge Road was reached.[30]

The Vineyard Nursery was most conveniently situated on the main road from London, and the eighteenth century saw the beginning of a time of great prosperity for the more enterprising and energetic nurserymen. Glass houses, hot houses and stoves were obviously an important and remunerative part of the Nursery business because of the fashion for collecting exotic plants.

'Stoves are contrivances for preserving such tender exotick Plants, which will not live in these northern Countries without artificial warmth in winter', wrote Philip Miller in the 1759 edition of his 'Dictionary'. He goes on to describe the two main types: 'Dry Stoves' which had heated pipes either in the floor or the back of the house, and 'Bark Stoves'. 'These have a large Pit, nearly the Length of the House, three Feet deep, and six or seven Feet wide, according to the Breadth of the House, which Pit is filled with fresh Tanners Bark, to make a hot Bed, and in the Bed the Pots of the most tender exotick trees, and herbaceous Plants, are plunged'.[31]

Labour was cheap – while James Lee could sell fuchsia plants at a guinea each he would be paying his gardeners less than 12s. a week. In 1793 Thomas Baird wrote 'The price of labour is much the same all over Middlesex men hired at 12s. a week in summer and 9s. in winter. Nursery men have their hands in general cheaper than common gardeners or farmers which can only be attributed to this, that their employment is more constant, more to be depended on, and perhaps less severe'.[32] About one man per acre was the usual number employed.

The popularity of exotic plants made intensive culture more important than extensive grounds, so that the 18 acres in Hammersmith and the additional ground in Fulham were sufficient for its needs until the great expansion took place at the end of the century under the second James Lee.

CHAPTER THREE

'Introduction to Botany'
and other publications

IN 1760 James Lee published *An introduction to Botany containing an explanation of the theory of that science and an interpretation
of its technical terms extracted from the works of Dr. Linnaeus and
calculated to assist such as may be desirous of studying that Author's
method and improvements*. James Lee is described on the title-
page as 'Nursery Man, at the Vineyard, at Hammersmith'.
The work was, in fact, largely a translation of the *Philosophia
Botanica* of Linnaeus. The last paragraph of the Preface says:

It now only remains for the Author to say something concerning his own Part in the Labour of this Undertaking. He is far from
desiring the World should conceive from the Appearance of his
Name in the Title Page, that he is of sufficient Strength to undertake a work of this kind without Assistance. Though it has always
been a Pleasure to him to study the Theory of his Profession, as
far as the Business of it would allow leisure for, he is very Sensible
of his own Inability to put the Materials of such a Work into a
Form correct enough to come under the Eye of the Public, and,
were he permitted, would readily acknowledge the Obligations he
has to those who have kindly helped him in this Undertaking, but
as some Injunctions oblige him to be silent on this Head, he must
content himself with having said this much to clear himself of any
Imputation of Presumption or Arrogance.

Ever since, there has been speculation as to who these
helpers were. Sir James Edward Smith, founder of the
Linnean Society and a friend of the Lee family, said that Lady
Ann Monson suggested that James Lee should undertake the
translation and helped him with it.[1]
Another candidate is Samuel Gray. In 1822 the applica-
tion to become a Fellow of the Linnean Society of a Dr. J. E.
Gray was rejected and he declared that this rejection was

16

rendered more bitter to him in that it was directed against 'the grandson of the Mr. Gray who translated the *Philosophia Botanica* of Linnaeus for his friend Mr. Lee, whose book first introduced the Swedish botanist's scientific writings to English readers'.[2] This 'Mr. Gray' was Samuel Gray the eldest son of Samuel Gray, a seedsman and importer of roots of Pall Mall, and elder brother of Edward Whitaker Gray (1747–1806), Keeper of the Department of Natural History of the British Museum. Little is known of him except that he was in the same business as his father and that he died in 1765 before his son, Samuel Frederick Gray, was born in 1766.[3] The last paragraph of the preface to the second edition of Lee's 'Introduction to Botany' published in 1765 reads:

To the Memory of a late ingenious and worthy Gentleman, the Author with Gratitude acknowledges the great Obligations he owed him, in putting the materials of the first Plan of this Work into a proper Form, and would willingly have informed the Public to whom he was obliged had he not been prohibited, while that Gentleman was living, from mentioning his Name and as it is uncertain that the surviving Relatives of that worthy Gentleman would like to see his name mentioned in a work of this kind, Prudence bids him be silent.

This gives support to the suggestion that it was Samuel Gray who helped Lee, but why a seedsman and root importer should decline to have his name associated with the work which brought the nurseryman Lee fame is difficult to understand. Edward Whitaker Gray certainly knew Lee and on at least one occasion gave him plants.[4] The tone of Lee's statement, too, suggests that his helpers were in a higher social station than himself. Lady Ann Monson died in 1776.

The second edition of Lee's *Introduction to Botany* contains the addition of a glossary taken from Berkenhout's *Botanical Lexicon* which had been published in 1764,[5] and a dedication to Dr. Linnaeus:

To the very Eminent Dr. Linnaeus.

Sir,

The permitting me to dedicate the following sheets to you, is the highest Point of my Ambition, and a Mark of my Gratitude and Esteem, for the Instruction and Pleasure I have received in the perusal of your truly learned and excellent Works. . . The 'Introduction to Botany' owes its first Principles to you, being collected from your Works, particularly the *Philosophia Botanica*,

17

nothing of it can be called mine, but its being cloathed in an English Dress; the addressing you in Front of my Book can therefore add nothing to your Instruction or Fame; your giving me Liberty to prefix your Name there does me the greatest Honour, at the same Time that it tells the World this Dedication is free from Interest and Flattery, as it is to you whom I have never seen, nor ever expect to see; my only Motive in this proceeds from a grateful sense of your superior merit, and to applaud you for the useful Lesson you have given to Mankind.

I am, with great Respect
Your most devoted
and obedient humble Servant
JAMES LEE.

A third edition was published in 1776 – it claimed to be 'corrected with large additions'; a fourth edition appeared in 1788, 'corrected with additions'; a fifth edition in 1794 was 'corrected'. The sixth in 1796[6] (a year after its author's death) claimed to be 'much improved and enlarged'; the Advertisement says 'Every edition of this Work for these last thirty years has been servilely copied from the second edition'. This edition was published in Edinburgh but an edition marked the fourth was also published in London in 1796. A so-called 'new edition, improved corrected and enlarged' appeared in 1799 also published in Edinburgh with additions by Charles Stewart; another edition 'corrected and revised by C. Stewart', appeared in 1806. The final edition, also called the fourth on the title page, but in fact the tenth, appeared in 1810. This contained a sketch of the life and writings of James Lee by Dr. Robert Thornton and claimed to have been 'corrected and enlarged by James Lee son and successor to the author'. It was dedicated to 'James Edward Smith M.D.' but in an undated letter to Sir James Edward Smith pasted in a copy of this edition in possession of the Linnean Society of London, James Lee, the younger, indignantly denies having anything to do with the work. The letter, published here by courtesy of the Linnean Society, is as follows:

Dear Sir,
I am desired by the publishers of Lee on Botany to send you a copy of that work; they applied to me sometime ago to have it published. I told them I had neither time or inclination to have any thing to do with it, but that they might do with it as they pleased. They have accordingly got up a New Edition and to my

18

surprise have added my name to it and Dr. Thornton has added yours; they have even made me dedicate it to you and added my name, which is an effrontery truly in unison with Paternoster Row. I have had no time to look it over, but if it is apiece with Mr. Lee's life, it must contain many blunders and falsehoods.

Hoping this meets you and Mrs. Smith in good health,
I am, Dr. Sir,
Yr. much obliged st.
JAMES LEE.

Lee's 'Introduction to Botany' was the first attempt to translate the works of Linnaeus into English. Thornton says 'the distinguishing merit of Lee's work is that it abounds with examples. There is scarce a single axiom laid down but four or five illustrations are given and this arose from his being practically acquainted not only with native plants . . . but also with exotic botany'.[7]

It was long regarded as a standard work. When, forty-seven years after its first publication, the *Edinburgh Review* reviewed *The Principles of Botany* by Willdernow, the writer referred to 'Lee's "Introduction to Botany" which has been longest in use in this country'.[8]

It was this work which made Lee famous and which attracted visitors from all over the world to the Vineyard Nursery. The 'work gave Mr. Lee a priority in his time that rendered his garden . . . the resort of all persons curious in botanical researches and added not a little to his fame and emoluments'.[9] Andrew Caldwell 'a beginner in botany', to use his own phrase, writing to Sir James Edward Smith in April, 1792, says 'Lee's "Introduction" in so far as it extends I find plain and useful'.[10]

The 1810 edition of Lee's 'Introduction to Botany' had as a frontispiece an engraving by Freeman of a portrait of James Lee made from an oil painting still in the possession of his descendants.* It also contained, as has been said, an account of his life by Dr. Thornton.

Dr. Robert John Thornton, who is best remembered for one of the most magnificent and romantic of all flower books, his *Temple of Flora*, which he ruined himself in publishing between 1799 and 1804, was the author of a number of books on botany.[11] It is likely that he undertook to write the sketch

* A reproduction of the original portrait forms the frontispiece to this work.

of Lee's life and to edit the book as 'hack work' when he was in great need of money – he did not scruple to advertise his own books in the footnotes to Lee's 'Introduction to Botany'.

He attributed two scientific observations to Lee. 'He discovered what islands had belonged to Europe and what to Asia by the heath (*Erica*) which is abundantly dispersed over Europe, Africa and America; but is not to be found in Asia or any of its islands which once formed part of that continent. . . . He generally observed, that, for want of insects to further the nuptials of plants, or a proper degree of ventilation, or rather favouring breezes, or from some defect in the escape of pollen from the anthers that the seeds in stove plants are in general unproductive, and for a series of years *artificial impregnation* has been performed at Hammersmith which always secured an increase, and proves the practical value of science'.

One rather odd story Thornton tells is best quoted in his own words: 'As might be expected from an author, Lee's Garden was always open to the curious; nor was he ever backward in communicating knowledge; whereas Mr. Miller concealed the names of his valuable collection in the Chelsea Gardens; and the papers, which contained his foreign seeds, were industriously thrown into the Thames, and such is the ardour of Botany, although the acquisition was often to be swam for, these were fished for up again and the names of the new plants then introduced, was thus known to Mr. Lee, and others, in a way which greatly surprised the author of the *Gardener's Dictionary*'.

When one considers that the Vineyard Nursery was some distance from the Thames and that Miller could easily have destroyed such wrappings instead of letting them float on the river this story seems likely to be one of the 'falsehoods' of which James Lee's son accused Thornton.

Five letters which Lee wrote to Linnaeus are preserved in the collections of the Linnean Society of London[12] and they show how great was his respect and admiration for the 'Father of Natural History' (as he addressed him in one). Writing, about 1766, he says 'The pleasure you have don me in begining a correspondence with me does me the greatest honour at the same time that it fills me with a sense of gratitude and you may for the future depend on my readyness to comply with any commands you shall be pleased to give me concerning plants and seeds'. The letters are concerned with the difficulties of sending live plants to Sweden, with requests that plants may be named in honour of various people, with descriptions of new plants and other botanical matters. Once only, at the end of the last letter of the series written October 4, 1776, does he express the affection and admiration he felt more openly. He writes 'The passion for plants in this Country encreases every Day and I have the pleasure to tell you that your *sexual system* is more and more admired, and by none more than your affectionate Friend and obedient humble Servant James Lee'.

In this same letter Lee remarks 'Mr. Banks'* Herbarium is certainly the greatest and I believe the best that ever was collected. It is the daily labour of many servants to paste them on paper, and Banks and Solander† spend 4 or 5 hours every day in describing and arranging them . . . Your old Friend Ellis is much decayed and seems tottering on the brink of the Grave'. Linnaeus had called Ellis 'The main support of Natural History in England'. This letter drew a very human retort from Linnaeus. 'You suppose Banks' Herbarium to be the largest anyone possesses but I should like to claim for mine that it is twice as large . . . I am very sorry about Ellis's condition but my own fate has the prior claim on me'. This was dated November 3, 1776. John Ellis had died on October 15, 1776. Linnaeus died on January 10, 1778.

Although no specimens from Lee are preserved in the Linnean Herbarium[13] the letters show that drawings made by his daughter Ann were sent. Linnaeus named a genus *Leea* after Lee. It is a genus of tropical plants belonging to the family *Vitaceae* including about seventy species. Sometimes they are placed in a family of their own *Leeaceae*. They are 'useful decorative plants for a warm greenhouse or stove. Some of them are much grown in the tropics for the beauty of their fruits' according to the Royal Horticultural Society's *Dictionary of Gardening*.

In addition to his 'Introduction to Botany' Lee published a pamphlet *Rules for collecting and preserving Seeds from Botany Bay* about 1787.[14] The list of botanical terms from his

* Sir Joseph Banks (1743–1820).
† Daniel Charles Solander (1736–82) librarian to Banks.

'Introduction to Botany' also appeared as a separate publication in 1813 under the title of *Termini Botanici*.

The Nursery published its catalogue in 1774 and James Lee is generally regarded as its author. It is a small book of seventy-six pages. Its contents are divided into Hardy trees and shrubs; Herbaceous plants; Greenhouse plants; Plants for a dry stove or glass house; Stove plants; Fruits; Kitchen garden seeds; Seeds of evergreen trees and shrubs, of deciduous trees and shrubs, of perennial flowers, of annual flowers, of biennial flowers; Seeds to improve land such as clover, trefoil, flax, hemp and lentils.

It throws some interesting light on the taste of the time. The 'Hardy trees and shrubs' include forty-eight kinds of roses; the 'Herbaceous plants' include many old favourites as well as many plants which we should regard as weeds and not cultivate in our gardens now that generations of skilled hybridizers have produced so many more dazzling varieties. In the eighteenth century it was enough that the plant should be new and rare. The greenhouse plants include fifty-four different varieties of *Mesembryanthemum* (a great favourite with James Lee); 'dry stove' plants include *Leea*. The kitchen garden seeds include those of Hammersmith green lettuce. All sorts of garden tools were also on sale.

CHAPTER FOUR

Plant introductions: The fuchsia

DURING the first half of the eighteenth century there was a great increase in the interest shown in garden flowers and many new plants were introduced – some 5,000 new species during the century.[1] Collecting new plants was a hobby for noblemen and landed gentry and many of them accumulated large collections. That there should be an enthusiasm for landscape gardening (where everything had to be informal and 'natural') at the same time as one for the collection and cultivation of exotic plants at first seems strange but perhaps both were an expression of the same wish to display something expensive, new and different. Nurserymen flourished. A number of the most successful of them were, like James Lee, Scottish; for example James Gordon of Mile End, Russel of Lewisham, and William Malcolm of Kennington. Philip Miller (whose father was born in Scotland) was accused by English gardeners of employing only Scotsmen and they banded together into a society and resolved that they, themselves, would not employ young men from the north. Their views were embodied in a pamphlet *Adam armed*.[2] This anti-Scottish feeling among English gardeners continued for years. In the year James Lee was born, 1715, Stephen Switzer was attacking 'Northern lads, which whether they have serv'd any Time in this Art or not, few of us know any thing of, yet by the Help of a little learning, and a great deal of Imprudence, they invade our *Southern* provinces ...'[3] No doubt there was business enough for all and no very active steps seem to have been taken to enforce the ban against Scottish gardeners.

Until 1783 when Lewis Kennedy died, the Vineyard Nursery was referred to as that of Messrs. Kennedy & Lee. As soon as they were established the partners began to introduce into England plants from abroad and correspondence was gradually established all over the world with people who would send back seeds. At that time it was very difficult to bring back living plants. It was reckoned that a hundred plants were lost for every one which survived of plants imported from the Far East until the Wardian case* was invented in 1842.[4]

The Vineyard Nursery specialized in exotic plants, that is plants not native of Europe, with the cultivation of which James Lee would have become familiar while employed by the Duke of Argyle. In 1794 Peter Foot surveying the agriculture of Middlesex says 'Lee's nursery at Hammersmith particularly for foreign plants is also of superior excellence'.[5] The following year Lysons wrote 'Lee and Kennedy who are noted for their successful culture of rare exotics and for introducing many new and beautiful plants have a nursery ground in this hamlet [Hammersmith] on the London road'.[6] James Lee's pamphlet *Rules for collecting and preserving Seeds from Botany Bay* shows some of the difficulties and the precautions which had to be taken. It is quoted in full from a copy in the Botany Library of the British Museum (Natural History):

Rules for collecting and preserving Seeds from Botany Bay.

In a country where all the plants are new to a European Botanist, and unknown to the Collector, the best method is to select the most beautiful, or those that are known to be of use in dying, mechanics, food or physic. Trees and shrubs are more particularly wanted; and herbaceous plants only for their beauty or the sweetness of their flowers.

The Collector should observe that every seed be perfectly ripened before it is gathered, and well dried, before it is folded up in the paper where it is to remain; every kind should be kept by itself, and some remarks wrote on the paper, whether it is a tree, shrub, or herbaceous plant. Those that have dry capsules, will keep best in the capsules, and those that have stones, like plums or peaches, will keep best divested of the pulp or outer coat; small seeds that shake from their capsules, need no other care than to be well dried before they are wrapped up in paper. When the collection is finished, the parcels should be packed in a close box with a layer of seeds and a layer of oakum alternately, till the box is filled. The tar rope will keep insects from preying on the seeds. The box should be nailed down very close, and covered with oil

---

* A glazed case containing soil in which plants could grow but which excluded air and moisture from outside, invented by N. B. Ward.

skin, to keep out damps and moisture, and kept in a dry part of the Ship.—Bulbous roots, such as lilies of all kinds, may be dug up and dried in the shade, then packed in a box with dry sand.

The flax plant may be planted in a box of earth; the bottom of the box should be bored full of holes and oyster shells laid over each hole, to drain off the moisture that would stagnate and rot the roots; then fill the box with earth, and plant the plants, giving them frequent waterings in their passage home. There may also be seeds sown in the box, which will vegetate in the passage. We can never expect this useful plant unless this method is taken, as the seeds are of so thin a texture, that they lose their vegetative quality before they can reach Europe.

Hortus Kewensis[7] names one hundred and thirty-five plants introduced into England, or first known as cultivated by, the Vineyard Nursery during the lifetime of James Lee.* They came from North America, from South Europe, from the Alps of Germany and Italy, from Siberia, the Cape of Good Hope, Chile, Canada, Austria, Madeira, Portugal, East Indies, Spain, New South Wales, China, the West Indies, Jamaica, Cayenne, Guinea, Sierra Leone, Greece and Mexico. Most of them would have come as seeds sent by correspondents abroad; later the Hammersmith Nursery sent out its own collectors.

The names of some of the correspondents are known. Professor Peter Simon Pallas 'Councillor of State to the Emperor of all the Russias, an eminent Naturalist and Traveller'[8] sent seeds of many valuable and rare plants from Russia, among them the 'Yellow Pontic Azalea' in 1792 and the 'Siberian Primrose' in 1794.[9]

A Mr. J. Pringle of Madeira collected plants and bulbs from the Cape of Good Hope between 1789 and 1795 and those he sent included ixias and gladiolus.[10] Mr. J. Elcock sent plants from Barbados between 1784 and 1789.[11]

Colonel William Paterson was another regular correspondent of the Nursery. He was in command of the company sent to protect convicts at Botany Bay when the first attempt to use Australia as a penal settlement was made. For a time he commanded a detachment stationed at Norfolk Island and both from Port Jackson and from Norfolk Island, sent back seeds. The Hammersmith Nursery owed plants such as the pleasantly named 'Silky Emboth' and 'Slender-stemmed

* See Appendix, pages 77–84.

25

Pogonia', as well as the 'Cape Marigold-leaved Goodenia' to him.[12]

He was an unusual soldier, being far more interested in botany than in his profession. As a young man he had explored part of South Africa and published an account as *A narrative of four journeys into the country of the Hottentots.* Later he became Governor of Australia.[13]

Even before Colonel Paterson went to Australia the Vineyard Nursery received seeds from the lands newly discovered and charted by Captain Cook; Joseph Banks, who knew James Lee well, had accompanied Captain Cook on his first voyage round the world and it was because of the number of specimens that he collected there that Botany Bay was so named. The Vineyard Nursery was the first to have seeds from Botany Bay; they were received in 1788.

'Saw-leaved Banksea' was the first plant to be raised from them and 'Thus has the pre-eminence of seniority here to all plants which have been introduced from thence to Great Britain' to use John Kennedy's own words.[14] For many years the Nursery specialized in 'New Holland plants' – New Holland being the early name for Australia. The *Kennedia*, the genus of plants named in honour of John Kennedy, were natives of Australia.[15]

Many plants were also received as gifts or through exchanges with other collectors.

In 1792 the Sierra Leone Company presented plants they had received from Sierra Leone.[16] The Dowager Lady de Clifford made a present of ixias in 1794;[17] the Honorable Mrs. Barrington gave plants raised from seeds received from Jamaica.[18]

The Nursery is said to have had the first China rose in 1789;[19] whether this is so or not the Nursery was widely known for its roses. The forty-eight kinds listed in the Catalogue of 1774 had increased to two hundred and twenty by 1808.[20] In 1784 Fabricius was 'particularly impressed'[21] with the display of roses.

James Lee was among the 'noblemen, gentlemen and others' who took part in a 'great interchange of exotic plants' with the Chelsea Gardens in 1771. The full list is as follows:

Her R.H. the Princess Dowager's garden at Kew
His Grace the Duke of Northumberland at Sion

26

Mr. Ord's at Walham Green
Dr. William Pitcairn's at Islington
Mr. Gordon's Nursery Garden at Mile-end
Mr. Lee's Nursery Garden at Hammersmith
Mr. Watson's Nursery Garden at Islington
Dr. John Fothergill's Garden at Upton
The Rt. Hon. the Earl of Coventry's
Richard Warner's Esq. at Woodford
Mr. Bewicke's at Clapham[22]

One notes that Mr. Lee (there is no mention of Kennedy) is put sixth on the list, but whether it is arranged according to the size of the collections exchanged or at random is not indicated.

Exchanges also took place with the Emperor of Austria's gardener at Schönbrun,[23] with M. Richard of the Paris Garden, [24] and with Thomas Louth of the Strasburg Botanic Garden.[25]

James Lee took advantage of every opportunity that presented itself to make contact with people abroad who would send him seeds. A letter to an unnamed acquaintance of his in Paris is preserved among the Egerton Manuscripts in the British Museum.

He writes:

Dear Sir,
    Mr. Sailsbury* who called on you at Paris tells me that you have a beautifull plant in your garden that comes from peru and that he thinks to be annual, if it should ripen any seeds I shall take it as a particular favour if you will send me some seeds. if you can think of anything that I can serve you in that is in my garden I shall serve you with great pleasure. my son & Daughter sends their respectfull compliments to you, and I am with great respect your most obliged and obedient humble servant
                                JAMES LEE
Vineyard Hammersmith
August 20 1786

In June of the same year he had written rather reproachfully to Colonel Bentham in Riga because he had put in an order for seeds too late:[26]

---

* Possibly Richard Anthony Salisbury (1761–1829), F.L.S. and first Secretary of the [Royal] Horticultural Society, who makes a number of acknowledgments to Lee & Kennedy in his works.

27

Dear Sir,

I received, and have sent your orders as soon as a Ship could be found, but should have wished you had given more early intiligence as I am afraid you can do nothing with the seeds till nixt Springe, we could not procure you any Tares* owing to the lateness of the Season having applyed in vain in all the London markets, and as the Casks was mesured to contain them, we was obliged to fill them up with two additional Bushels of Rygrass. Grass seeds was never so scarce as it is this Season, being nearly Double the price that it is in Common years. In regard to the plants it is impossible to send them at this season, they should either go early in the Spring or Autumn, and we shall endeavour to send them at the proper season. . .

He continues by listing the contents of the two casks being sent to Colonel Bentham in the care of Mr. Tromponsky at Riga. They contained seeds of red and white clover, rye grass, field turnip, beans and 'saint foine'.† After mention of a Mr. Henderson,‡ who had also written, John Aitton 'an ingenous man and a good gardener, I suppose the best you have in Russia', a Captain Brine who 'is not yet arrived in the port of London', and one further reproach to Colonel Bentham for not sending his order in time, James Lee cannot resist adding

If you have any opportunity of collecting Seeds I will endavour to make a proper return for them. I particularly want seeds of Rhodadenron Dauricum, R. Chrysanthum and Azalea lutea.

Colonel Bentham was Sir Samuel Bentham, a naval architect and engineer who travelled extensively in Russia and lived there for a time; he was a brother of Jeremy Bentham the philosopher.

The plant with which the name of the Hammersmith Nursery is most often associated, the fuchsia, was not introduced by Lee & Kennedy but they were the first nursery to make it available for sale. Many different versions of the story of how the fuchsia was obtained by Lee & Kennedy have been published. The earliest to give any detail is that which appeared on the front page of the *Lincoln Herald* of November 4, 1831 and was reprinted in *Notes and Queries* September 1, 1894. The authority for it is given as 'Mr.

---

* Common vetch (*Vicia sativa*).

† Sainfoin (*Onobrychis viciifolia*) a fodder crop.

‡ Probably Logan Henderson, botanist to the Tsar.

Shepherd the respectable and informed concervator of the Botanical Gardens at Liverpool'.

John Shepherd was appointed Curator to the Liverpool Botanic Gardens in 1802.[27] In 1803 he was in London visiting nursery gardens with introductions from Sir James Edward Smith[28], who would certainly have included the Hammersmith Nursery among them because he knew the Lee family well and had actually lived in a house opposite the Nursery for a time.[29] It is possible therefore that John Shepherd obtained the story direct from James Lee's son only fourteen years after the event. Shepherd was still alive in 1831 when the *Lincoln Herald* published its story and he made no comment on it in subsequent issues. It is the only version which can be traced back in this way. It is quoted below as it appears in the *Lincoln Herald* except that the 'fucia' of the *Herald* has been changed to the correct form of 'fuchsia', the plant having been named in honour of Leonhard Fuchs.

Old Mr. Lee, a nurseryman and gardener near London, well-known fifty or sixty years ago, was one day showing his variagated treasures to a friend, who suddenly turned to him and declared, 'Well, you have not in your collectoin a prettier flower than I saw this morning at Wapping.' 'No! and pray what is this phoenix like?' 'Why, the plant was elegant, and the flowers hung in rows like tasels from the pendant branches, their colour the richest crimson, in the centre a fold of deep purple', and so forth. Particular directions being demanded and given, Mr. Lee posted off to the place, where he saw, and at once perceived that the plant was new in this part of the world. He saw and admired. Entering the house, 'My good woman, this is a nice plant. I should like to buy it.' 'Ah, sir, I could not sell it for no money, for it was brought me from the West Indies by my husband, who has now left again and I must keep it for his sake'. 'But I must have it'. 'No, Sir!' 'Here' (emptying his pockets) 'here is gold, silver and copper'—his stock was something more than eight guineas. 'Well-a-day, but this is a power of money, sure and sure'. "Tis yours, and the plant is mine and my good dame shall have one of the first young ones I rear to keep for your husband's sake'. 'Alack, alack!' 'You shall, I say'. A coach was called in which was safely deposited our florist and his seemingly dear purchase. His first work was to pull off and utterly destroy every vestage of blossom and blossom-bud, it was divided into cuttings which were forced into bark beds and hot beds, were re-divided and sub-divided. Every effort was used to multiply the plant. By the commencement of the next flowering season Mr. Lee was the delighted possessor of three hundred fuchsia plants all giving promise of blossom. The two which opened first were removed to his show house. A lady came. 'Why Mr. Lee, my dear Mr. Lee, where did you get this charming flower?' 'Hem! 'tis a new thing my lady – pretty! 'tis lovely.' 'Its price?' 'A guinea; thank your ladyship', and one of the two plants stood proudly in her ladyship's boudoir. 'My dear Charlotte! where did you get' etc. 'Oh!'tis a new thing I saw it at old Mr. Lee's. Pretty, is it not?' 'Pretty!'tis beautiful! Its price?' 'A guinea; there is another left.' The visitor's horses smoked off to the suburb; a third flowering plant stood on the spot where the first had been taken. The second guinea was paid and the second chosen fuchsia adorned the drawing room of her second ladyship. The scene was repeated as new-comers saw and were attracted by the beauty of the plant. New chariots flew to the gates of old Lee's nursery grounds. Two fuchsias, young, graceful and bursting into healthy flower were constantly seen on the same spot in his repository. He neglected not to gladden the faithful sailor's wife by the promised gift, but ere the flower season closed three hundred golden guineas clinked in his purse, the produce of a single shrub of the widow in Wapping, the reward of the taste, decision, skill and perseverance of old Mr. Lee.

The narrator seems to have allowed his love of a good story to run away with him – one notes that the wife at Wapping becomes a widow in the course of it – but it is not necessary to believe that the first purchaser of the fuchsia was a Lady Charlotte to accept the story as correct in essentials. This fuchsia is believed to have been *Fuchsia coccinea*, a native of Chile described by Aiton in *Hortus Kewensis* in 1789 and said by Curtis in his *Botanical Magazine* of 1792 to have been given to Kew by a Captain Firth in 1788. Curtis adds 'Mr. Lee of Hammersmith we understand first had this plant for sale'.

There are a number of alternative versions of how James Lee got the fuchsia plant; some say it came from his own collector in South America;[30] others that he got it from his friend Aiton of Kew, unofficially, and used the story of finding it at Wapping to cover up.[31] In yet other versions of the Wapping story the woman concerned became the *mother*[32] of a sailor boy who brought back the plants and in one her son is even named as Thomas Hogg,[33] who is said to have brought the plant home from San Domingo. (This, however, seems to have resulted from some confusion in dates since a Thomas Hogg of New York is known to have sent seeds of fuchsia home from San Domingo in 1873.[34]) One account says that Lee paid the sailor's mother eighty guineas.[35] All agree that

Lee raised three hundred plants and sold them at a guinea a plant except the *Floricultural Cabinet* of 1855, which says '£10-20 a plant'.

In passing it may be noted that Lee might have visited Wapping in connection with plants he was sending abroad, since on occasions plants from the Vineyard Nursery were shipped from there; for example in 1776 the *Poly Jones* was at Wapping with plants from Lee's being sent to France.[36] A part of the riverside at Hammersmith used to be known as 'Little Wapping',[37] but there is no reason to believe that this is the Wapping of the story.

According to Thornton 'Lee might have died rich, but he was notoriously generous, and cared not what expenses he was at for the attainment of rare plants, and when he possessed such as might have procured him a golden harvest, he chose rather to give duplicates away to lovers of Botany, before selling them to the rich but careless collectors of flowers, rather led to them through ostentation than from a laudable enthusiasm in the pursuit of knowledge'. This generosity, which seems strange in a nurseryman, if not in a botanist, is mentioned by others. Fabricius comments on it* and R. A. Salisbury writes of 'Messrs. Lee & Kennedy whose liberality in giving specimens of their rarest plants to Botanists does them so much honour'.[38]

Over two hundred years have passed since James Lee first introduced new plants into England; few of the heaths, gladiolus, ixias, pelargoniums and the rest which we now cultivate are the varieties he knew, although some may be their progeny. Many of the exotic plants he specialized in are beyond the means of any save the few today but two, at least of the plants he introduced can still be found in nurserymen's catalogues – *Buddleia globosa*, a shrub with honey-scented flowers like orange balls, and *Primula marginata*, a lavender-blue alpine primrose.

* See page 33.

CHAPTER FIVE

Patrons and friends

MANY travellers who came to London during his lifetime visited James Lee at his nursery garden and some have left accounts of their visits. A regular visitor, when he was in England, was John Christian Fabricius, a famous Danish entomologist and economist and pupil of Linnaeus, later professor of natural history, economy and finance at Kiel. He first visited London in 1767 when he was twenty-two; there he met Dr. Daniel Charles Solander, who had been the favourite pupil of Linnaeus and who was then employed at the British Museum as assistant in Natural History.

Fabricius says 'To him I am indebted as well for the benefit as the pleasure I enjoyed during my stay in England. He introduced me to the scientific clubs, and procured the acquaintance and connection with all the learned persons in our department, [*i.e.*, natural history] viz., Banks, the two Hunters,* Fordyce,† Lee, Drury,‡ Lady Ann Monson, Eaton,§ Fothergill, Webb,‖ Ellis, Pennant,¶ Greville,** and many others whose houses and libraries and collections were soon opened to me'. Fabricius had a great love for England and came as often as he could; he spent every summer from 1772 to 1775 in England and returned again in 1780, 1782, 1787 and 1791.[1]

He wrote an account of his 1782 visit to his 'old friend Lee'

* John Hunter (1728–93), surgeon, and William Hunter (1755–1812), physician.
† George Fordyce (1736–1802), physician.
‡ Dru Drury (1725–1803), entomologist.
§ Possibly Daniel Isaac Eaton (d.1814), bookseller.
‖ Probably Philip Carteret Webb (1700–1770), antiquary.
¶ Thomas Pennant (1726–1798), naturalist and traveller and correspondent of Linnaeus.
** Charles Francis Greville (1749–1802), one of the founders of the [Royal] Horticultural Society.

32

in the eighth letter of his *Briefe aus London vermischten Inhalts* which he published in 1784. First he visited Kew and then 'On the way back we paid a visit in Hammersmith, a little place six miles from London, to my old friend Lee who has a sizeable garden here and who does a very considerable trade in plants and seeds. He has fine plantations of various sorts of firs, pines and other trees which the English use in laying out their parks, including a large number of exotic growth. He is a man especially worth visiting by foreigners because of his frank, friendly and affable disposition. He has the knowledge of the true botanist and is never happier than when imparting this to others. He shows them all his different plants, is generous in giving away cuttings and seedlings, and contributes in every way he can to the spread of botanical knowledge. His "Introduction to Botany", of which he has recently brought out a new edition, contains an excellent exposition of the Linnean system (of classification) and of Linnaeus' "Philosophia Botanica". It is on this account that Linnaeus in his taxonomy created in his honour the name *Leea*. This time I was particularly impressed with his display of roses which is extraordinarily large and varied and exhaled a delicious scent. I have known him since my first visit to England, and both on that occasion and each time since that I have been in London he has been a helpful friend and companion on our excursions in the district round about. We have usually planned these for a Sunday, since on weekdays he could hardly have managed to leave his garden and his work.

'He is in addition a keen entomologist and has an extensive collection partly from native and partly from foreign sources. Most of the new specimens in this I have already identified and described ...

'Lee is a Scot like almost all seedsmen and gardeners in and around London. The Scots have established almost a monopoly in this occupation to the virtual exclusion of the English, and businesses are handed on from one Scot to another. The same is true of bakers. The vast majority of London bakers are from Scotland and they do not let the trade go out of their hands.

'We got back to London that evening without mishap although the hour was late and it was pretty dark. The damp rainy evening was our protection. English robbers, those on horseback that is, known as Highwaymen, waylay travellers only in fine weather. In bad weather they do not venture forth and the robbers on foot, known as footpads, could not so easily molest us in our postchaise.'[2]

In his main work *Entomologia systematica emendata et aucta* published in four volumes between 1792 and 1794 he lists among the collections he has used that of 'Lee Hammersmith'. Lee's collection included insects from Africa, the Cape of Good Hope, India, America and Brazil as well as native ones. Paintings of twenty of the most beautiful of the butterflies in Lee's collection (some of them described by Fabricius) form a luxurious folio volume by an unknown artist entitled *Coloured specimens to illustrate the natural history of butterflies* which was published by William Miller in 1806. According to the Introduction 'The object of this work is to give accurate and highly finished delineations of the Genus Papilio, according to the system of Linnaeus. The specimens are all coloured by the same person, who made the drawings from the original specimens, and consequently the number of copies that come before the Public, will be very limited; they cannot exceed fifty . . .'

Another visitor, Carl Thunberg, was a fellow student with Fabricius under Linnaeus (whose son he succeeded to the Chair of Botany in Uppsala University), naturalist and traveller; he visited England in 1778. He says, 'I farther saw during my short abode in this country every thing worthy of notice, especially as to Natural History. . . I made several excursions in the vicinity of London, to see the beautiful gardens of Kew, abounding with living plants and under the care of Mr. Aiton: Mr. Lee's garden which is uncommonly rich in trees and shrubs: Dr. Fothergill's garden, Chelsea, etc. At Mr. Lee's I likewise saw his daughter's fine collection of Insects, which had been increased with the uncommonly beautiful Insects from the Coast of Bengal, which Lady Monson had collected there, and, previous to her death, bequeathed to Miss Lee'.[3]

Another visitor to the Nursery was Pierre-Joseph Redouté, the botanical artist, who spent some months in London in 1786–7.[4] He was then a young man of twenty-seven. Banks helped him as he did almost anyone who needed help in the field of science. Redouté drew most of the plates in *Sertum*

Anglicum, Bouquet Anglais ou Plantes rares observées en 1786 et 1787, which pictured rare plants growing at Kew. The text of this work was by L'Heritier de Brutelle, a wealthy French botanist whose companion Redouté was; L'Heritier de Brutelle corresponded with Lee and sent him plants.[5] Redouté stayed with the Lee family for part of the time and gave James Lee one of his paintings of a Campanula by way of thanks.[6] Redouté was to become artist to the Empress Josephine and to immortalize the plants cultivated at La Malmaison in some of the most magnificent of all flower books. It may have been on his recommendation that John Kennedy (who was his own age) was called in to advise the Empress. André Michaux, another French botanist, also visited Lee and sent seeds to Banks to be grown by Lee in recognition of civilities shown him when in England.[7]

Native botanists, too, found the Hammersmith Nursery worth a visit. In 1779 Thomas Woodward* visited Mr. Lee and on his return mentioned his visit in a letter dated August 15 written from Great Berkhamstead Castle, to William Curtis (the founder of the *Botanical Magazine*); he says 'Mr. Lee whom I saw that day [*i.e.*, the day before he left town] and whose civility I can never enough thank him for, mentioned that he wanted the *Parnassia* it grows in the meadows here and I intend getting some roots for him. . . .'[8]

A visitor to the Nursery in 1794 proved less welcome. He was Adrian Hardy Haworth, who devoted Chapter III of his book *Observations on the genus Mesembryanthemum*, published 1794–5, to an account of his visits. Although the previous year he had published a work entitled *Botanical history of Rhus Toxicodendron*, at that time he was unknown as a botanist; before his death in 1833 he was to achieve recognition as an authority on succulent plants. The *Mesembryanthemum*, or fig-marigold, is a genus of succulent plants, mostly natives of South Africa, with fleshy leaves and white or brightly coloured daisy-like flowers. It was popular in the eighteenth century and James Lee was particularly attached to it. His 1774 Catalogue had listed fifty-four kinds and since then, as a letter of his to Linnaeus shows, he had raised new varieties.

---

* Thomas Woodward (c.1745–1820), a botanist and part author of *British Fuci*.

Haworth was twenty-six at the time of his visit and James Lee seventy-nine. His account is as follows:

'Early in the spring of the present year [1794], I went to Hammersmith to solicit the favour of seeing Mr. Lee's *Mesembryanthema*, for I had heard he had got the first collection of them about London; but although I found he had many rare and nondescript species I also found his collection wanted a great number of the sorts which I have since seen flourish in his Majesty's matchless collection at Kew.

'When I arrived at the nursery, I was fortunate enough to meet with the foreman of the ground whose civility induced him to shew me all the *Mesembryanthema* he was acquainted with; but as he could not satisfactorily tell me, which of the sorts were, and which were not described, I fell much short of the information I sought; for only seeing the plants in a cursory manner without any book on the spot, and being at that time unacquainted with a great many of the Kew catalogue species, I found myself when I got home unable either to describe properly the new sorts from memory, (after so slight a first view) or, to distinguish with sufficient precision which were nondescripts and which were already described, and the incongruous vague or rejected names. . . which were applied to some sorts and which sounded harsh in my memory rather tended to increase my confusion than develop the plants.

'But not disheartened by a few difficulties, I again went to Hammersmith in June last, and thought myself exceedingly lucky to find Mr. Lee (Senior) in the ground; of whom (after introducing myself to him as a general Botanist) I requested the favour of being permitted to view his *Mesembryanthema*, adding, that I was particularly attached to that tribe of plants, and by way of compliment told him I had heard much both of the rarity, and the number of the sorts he cultivated.

'After desiring me to stay while he went to and returned from the house, he shewed me the plants and by way of trying my strength, I suppose, asked me the names of a great many more sorts than he condescended to tell me the names of.

'I took the liberty of endeavouring to set him right on the names of one or two of the *Mesembryanthema* described by Linnaeus in *Species Plantarum*. . . at which he was evidently chagrined and affected to smile at the idea of *my* attempting to teach *him* the names of a set of plants he said he had been accustomed to consider himself familiar with from his youth. I endeavoured to explain matters but my remonstrance was not attended to. The chagrin I thus innocently occasioned was the foundation of the incivility he shewed me when I went to Hammersmith again in August, with an intention of examining some of the sorts; which I have not to this day seen the flowers of, and am most doubtful about, and which I knew he would have in bloom about that time, from having observed them preparing for it when I was there in June.

'I went in August, I say, to Hammersmith again a third and last time, and thought myself particularly fortunate in finding Mr. Lee (Senior) again walking about the nursery; I addressed him in the chearful language of politeness and civility, and again solicited permission to look at his plants; when, remembering the little respect I had already appeared to pay to one or two of his names of *Mesembryanthema* he answered me by uttering something like the word *well*, in a tone of voice almost as unintelligible, as it was unwelcoming, and immediately walked along the path he was in and then turned off to the left to a man at work; to whom I very naturally conjectured he was giving instructions, and from whom I as naturally supposed, he would either return to me; send a man to show me the plants or a message permitting me to see them alone, or otherwise a denial to view them at all; which last indeed, I did by implication tacitly receive; for he neither returned to me himself, nor sent a message; but suffered me to wander about the principal walk which leads to the Turnpike until I was tired of waiting; after which (saturated with disappointment and affront) I came away, without being permitted to look at a single thing I wished to see, but not without forming *two* resolutions; one, to record the behaviour which occasioned my perplexity, the other to return to the scene of it no more'.

Poor Haworth, smarting under the snub and hastening to get what revenge he could by putting the story of his visits on record can never have paused to consider that the effect on his readers might be other than he intended, or that the portrait he had painted of himself was far from attractive! One's sympathies are with Mr. Lee, since few seventy-nine year old experts are likely to enjoy being 'set right' by unknown twenty-six year olds! It is interesting to note that Mr. Lee was to be found about the nursery grounds in the last years of his life.

A visitor who was at the Nursery the month before James Lee died was L'Abbe Jose Francisco Correa de Serre. Tantalizingly enough in his letter to Sir James Edward Smith written July 4, 1795, he gives an account of experiments he made with various species of *Verbascum*, or mullein, growing there, testing the 'phenomena of their irritability with the greatest success', but he makes no mention of James Lee himself at all.[9] Perhaps by that time he was no longer well enough to be out in his garden.

The notorious Lady Craven, who was later to become the Margravine of Anspach and Bayreuth and for whom her second husband, the Margrave, was to purchase the largest house in the Hammersmith district, Brandenburgh House, owned a small house in Fulham by the river called Craven Cottage. In February, 1786 (?) she wrote from St. Petersburgh to a Dr. Budd 'As to my cottage. . . I would have a great many vines planted at the cottage – as there is one which produced the very best grapes I ever eat in any country, owing to the shelterd situation – and all of the same sort – I beg there may be no alteration in the disposition of the planting etc. – only the willows cut away properly – as your residence is in London, this cottage will be an agreeable circumstance to you. . .'

As a postscript she adds 'P.S. Mr. Lee, the great Botanist at Hammersmith had best be consulted in planting the grapes . . . Mr. Lee lives at Hammersmith. Lee and Kennedy is wrote over their garden. Give my comps. to Lee – he knows me very well and is the best person to consult.'[10]

An even more distinguished patron of the Hammersmith Nursery was Thomas Jefferson, the author of the Declaration of Independence and the third President of the United States, who sent plants from the Hammersmith Nursery to the value of £4 15s. to a friend in Tours on April 24, 1786. Jefferson also had a copy of Kennedy & Lee's 'Catalogue of plants and seeds' in his library.[11]

The Duke of Orleans purchased all the trees and shrubs for his estate at Monçeaux from the Hammersmith Nursery.[12]

Another customer was Edmund Davall, a botanist who lived in Switzerland and corresponded with Sir James Edward Smith for many years. He mentioned his intention of buying 'roots' from Lee in a letter dated March 11, 1791.[13]

The skill of Messrs. Lee & Kennedy in dealing with exotic plants was well known. About 1798 a young man, Mr. Francis North, purchased in Portugal a number of plants of a fine species of *Moraea* from the gardens of the late Queen of Portugal, intending them for his mother. Mrs. North, described by John Kennedy as 'the elegantly tasted Mrs. North, lady to the Right Hon. the Lord Bishop of Winchester to whose fervor and liberality in botanical pursuits we owe much of the present prevailing taste for the science' was keenly interested in rare and unusual plants. By the time her son reached home, however, only one plant was still alive. 'Immediately on its arrival it was consigned in a very sickly state to the care of Messrs. Lee and Kennedy who had the good fortune to recover it'.[14] The plant was named *Moraea Northiana*, no doubt in honour of Mrs. North.

Another story of James Lee's skill and quickness in perceiving possibilities is told by William Curtis.

One day when James Lee was looking through some dried specimens of plants, recently received by Sir Joseph Banks from the Cape of Good Hope, he noticed a geranium with an unusual spear-shaped leaf of a kind never before seen in this country. Examining the specimen carefully he saw that it included a few seeds; Banks willingly gave them to him and from them he raised the only plants of the species seen in England.[15]

Whether Lady Ann Monson should be regarded as a friend, or a patron, of James Lee is difficult to decide. She suggested and helped him with his 'Introduction to Botany'[16] and her name was sufficiently linked with his for his daughter's name (with that of Dr. Fothergill) to appear on her portrait which is shown on the wall in the Cruickshank caricature of a Royal Horticultural Society meeting.[17] She also left her collection of Bengal insects to his daughter Ann.[18] It is possible that Ann was, in fact, named after her. She is mentioned twice by Lee in letters to Linnaeus, firstly when he thanks Linnaeus on her behalf for the compliment of a plant being named *Monsonia Speciosa* in her honour and secondly when he apologizes because Lady Monson has forgotten to notify Linnaeus of some plants put on board a Swedish ship for him so that it is probable they have all died.[19]

Thunberg, who met her in 1774 at the Cape of Good Hope, when she was on her way to Bengal, gives a vivid impression of her. He says, 'She was a lady about sixty years of age, who amongst other languages, had also a knowledge of Latin, and had, at her own expense brought with her a draughtsman in order to assist her in collecting and delineating scarce specimens of natural history.[20] She died in India two years later.

John Kennedy paid his tribute to her in a rather more formal passage which forms part of his description of *Monsonia filia*, or 'Hairy-leaved Monsonia', in the *Botanist's Repository:*

'The Genus Monsonia was formed by Linnaeus in honour of the Right Hon. Lady Ann Monson whose enthusiasm in pursuing the study of natural history, knew no bounds, and whose liberal and fostering hand contributed more, perhaps, than any of her cotempories, by her encouragement and example to the then incipient but not so prevailing taste for the study of botany. .'[21]

Monsonia filia was a native of the Cape of Good Hope introduced into England by Lee & Kennedy in 1788. Having a plant named in one's honour was a privilege much sought after in the late eighteenth century when plants were being discovered, examined and systematically named in accordance with the Linnean binomial system, in a manner never before attempted. Linnaeus named a genus *Leea* in honour of James Lee and three of Lee's letters to him deal with the same subject. The one concerning Lady Monson has already been mentioned.

In October 1772 Lee wrote:

I know Mr. Miller sent you a drawing of a plant he wanted you to name after my great friend Dr. John Fothergill, you say that you have already named it *Anamalis* but if it is not already printed I beg you would be so good to alter it in favour of my friend for the Doctor is fond of that plant as it is sweet and elegant and will indure in the open air in the severest of winters; however if this cannot be comply'd with, I beg you will name a plant after him that will stand abroad in England the whole year, and if shruby and elegant so much the better. Doctor John Fothergill is one of the greatest promoters of Natural History (particularly botany) that we have in this countrey, he is a physician of the first Rank in the Metropolis of London, a man of great Learning and posessed of every good quality that constitutes the great and wise man. He is posessed of a most elegant garden with a fine collection of curious plants; he collects every part of Natural History from all parts of the Globe and would very willingly communicate anything to you that he has, worthy of your acceptance if you will be so good to send an imediate answer to this. I will communicate to you every thing that I have that is new and curious. I am wise Sir your most obedient humble servant.

JAMES LEE, Nurseryman at Hammersmith Vineyard, Hammersmith.[22]

Fothergill's biographer says 'About 1774 Linnaeus gave the name *Fothergilla* to a genus of hardy deciduous shrubs with scented flowers which Fothergill had obtained from the southern provinces of America'.[23]

Dr. Fothergill was among the well known personalities of the London of his time; he was a Quaker and founder of Ackworth School but his main interests were scientific; he had a botanical garden at Upton in Essex which included a 'suite of Hot and Green-House appartments of nearly 260 feet in extent, containing upwards of 3,400 distinct species of exotics'.[24] The catalogue of the sale of his plants in 1781, after his death, fills fifty pages and the plants took three days to sell. Not only did he have agents in China, Hindustan, East Indies and Siberia who would send him seeds but he sent out collectors himself.[25] It was at his request that William Bartram embarked on his exploration of the Floridas, Carolina and Georgia.[26]

There is rather different feeling about the short letter Lee wrote to Linnaeus in October 1775 saying that Miss Blackburne of Orford had 'for sometime importuned' him to send Linnaeus an undescribed plant and ask him to name it in her honour. He encloses a drawing his daughter has made of such a plant and its description and asks Linnaeus to 'Honour Miss Blackburne with a name'.

Miss Anne Blackburne was another of the ladies who collected natural history specimens. She 'made natural history her favourite study and delight. Her own collections of birds, insects, corals and shells is extensive and contains many species of rare and curious productions arranged in her museum at Fairfield'.[27]

It was the Forsters, however, who named *Blackburnia* in honour of John Blackburne and his daughter Anne.[28]

Another close friend of James Lee was Sydney Parkinson, a Scotsman and artist, whose relationship with the Lee family is dealt with in Chapter VII.

Francis Masson was another Scottish friend of James Lee who wrote to Linnaeus of him as 'my friend Francis Masson'.[29]

Masson was the first collector to be sent abroad by the Royal Botanic Gardens, Kew, and, as with so many scientific ventures of the period, the suggestion that he should go was made by Banks. He made three journeys in South Africa between 1772 and 1774 collecting seeds, and in 1776 he visited the Canaries, Azores, Madeira, and the West Indies. In 1781 he returned to England and remained there for two years. After travelling to Portugal and Madeira in 1786 he went back to the Cape and remained there for the next ten years collecting.[30]

Returning to England in 1795 he prepared for publication his *Stapeliae Novae, or A collection of severall new species of that genus discovered in the interior parts of Africa.* This was a work in two volumes dedicated to King George III. The *Stapeliae* are a genus of leafless succulent plants with angled stems and reddish brown or purple flowers which have an unpleasant smell which gives them their English name of 'Carrion flower'.

In his preface Masson says 'Two species of *Stapelia* were heretofore described by Botanists; the genus now promises a numerous harvest of species. In my various journeys through deserts I have collected about forty and these I humbly present to lovers of Botany. The figures were drawn in their native climate, and though they have little to boast in point of art, they possibly exhibit the natural appearance of the plants they represent, better than figures made from subject growing in exotic houses can do'.

The two volumes published in 1796 and 1797 contain forty-one plates, Latin descriptions of each with 'some useful hints annexed', in Masson's own words.

Masson gave James Lee nearly a hundred of the drawings he made at the Cape – most are of plants but two are lively illustrations of waterfalls. These drawings were presented by

James Lee's great grandson, James Lee, to the Botany Library of the British Museum (Natural History) in 1885.[31]

Hortus Kewensis records the very large number of plants introduced into cultivation by Masson and his name was given to a genus of plants by Linnaeus. A variety of heath he introduced in 1788 from the Cape was named *Erica Leeana* or 'Lee's Heath', no doubt in honour of his friend.[32] He died aged sixty-five in Canada where he had been sent in 1798.

Writing to Sir James Edward Smith in March 1806 James Lee's son says:

> We are Sorry to have to communicate to you of our dear friend Masson, who died at Montreal in January last. We lament his fate most sincerely. He was very hardly dealt by, in being exposed to the bitter cold of Canada in the decline of life, after twenty-five years services in a hot climate, – and all for a pittance. He has done much for botany and science, and deserves to have some lasting memorial given of his extreme modesty, good temper, generosity, and usefulness. We hope when opportunity serves you will be his champion.[33]

Writing again in July to Smith, James Lee (the younger) returns to the subject 'Masson was of a mild temper, persevering in his pursuits even to a great enthusiasm, of great industry, which his specimens and drawings of fish, animals, insects, plants, of views of the countries he passed through, evince; and though he passed a solitary life in distant countries from society his love of natural history never forsook him. Characters like him seem for the present dwindling in the world, but I trust they will revive'.[34]

James Lee (the younger) was under twenty when Masson began his journeys so that Masson must have spent much of his time during his visits to England with the Lee family for the younger man to have come to feel such an affectionate regard for him and to be so indignant on his behalf.

James Lee also knew Sir Joseph Banks well. When one considers the extent and variety of Joseph Banks's activities it seems odd that his name is so little known to the general reader today. He was born in 1743 and became interested in botany while he was still at Eton; he went on a voyage to Newfoundland collecting plants and to Iceland as well as round the world with Captain Cook; he founded the King's garden at Kew as a botanical garden; he had the cultivation of tea introduced to India from China; he helped to found both the Linnean Society of London and the Royal Horticultural Society; he was president of the Royal Society for forty-two years and, as holder of that office, a Trustee of the British Museum. He played a part in the settlement of Australia – it was at his suggestion that convicts were sent to Botany Bay, a name given to the area because he had found so many botanical specimens there when he landed with Captain Cook.[35] On his death in 1820 he left a life interest in his scientific collections and library to his librarian, Robert Brown; after Brown's death they were to go to the British Museum. Brown, however, gave them to the Museum at once and was himself employed there to look after them.[36] (Many of the books consulted in the writing of this work come from the Banks library and bear a small stamp 'Jos. Banks'.)

Banks was a generous patron and friend of anyone who was interested in any aspect of science – at one time it was usual to suggest that Banks himself possessed little scientific knowledge but those competent to judge now suggest that he was a scientist of no mean order himself.[37] When he grew old he became autocratic and intolerant of opposition. He was twenty-eight years younger than James Lee and consulted him on more than one occasion.

In a letter to him dated April 25, 1776, James Lee recommended a young gardener, David Nelson, as a suitable person to go on a voyage with Captain Cook and take care of plants and seeds which would be collected for Banks during the voyage. James Lee wrote

Vineyard 25 April 1776

Honoured Sir,

I have sent you the bearer David Nelson as a proper person for the purpose you told me of, he knows the general runn of our collections of plants about London understands something of botany but doe's not pretend to know much knowledge in it – I have inquired particularly into his character, and find him exactly suited for the purpose of a collector.

I have injoined him to secrecy whither you make a bargin with him or not one thing he desired me to mention which is he will want a little advance money to rigg him out. I am Dear Sir with the greatest regard your obedient Humble Servant

JAMES LEE

A mysterious postscript follows:

P.S. I have a better opinion of this man than B – kie, which is with other Reasons that I shall tell you at meeting – the Reason I did not send him.[38]

Possibly this 'B – kie' was the Blaikie whom Lee recommended to the Comte de Lauraguais later the same year and extracts from whose diary are quoted below.[39]

Nelson proved a success and in a letter written on March 30, 1787, to Lord Sandwich Banks himself recommended him. He says:

He sailed with Captain Cook on his third voyage round the world in my service for the purpose of collecting plants and seeds and was eminently successful in the object of his mission. He had been regularly educated as a gardener and learned there the art of taking care of plants at sea and guarding against the many accidents to which they are liable which few people but himself have had the opportunity to know practically. He learned also how to conduct himself on board ship and made acquaintance with the inhabitants of the South Sea Islands and their language which will in all probability facilitate his obtaining the number of plants wanted.[40]

This recommendation had tragic consequences for Nelson, for the voyage he was to undertake was that intended to introduce the breadfruit tree to the West Indies. The Captain of the ship was Captain William Bligh and the ship *The Bounty*. During the voyage mutiny broke out on board. The mutineers, among whom William Brown, the assistant gardener, also chosen by Banks, was prominent, set Nelson adrift and he died as a result of exposure in 1789 at Keopang in Indonesian Timor north-west of Darwin, Australia. Brown himself was murdered on Pitcairn Island.[41]

Banks also consulted James Lee when in 1790 the Woolly Aphis, *Eriosoma lanigera* made its first appearance in England. Banks wrote, 'Mr. Lee had them abundantly . . . and was much alarmed for the mischief they threatened. . .Nov. 9 1790 called at Mr. Lee's at Hammersmith. He told me that all his young apple trees were full of insects, and that he was at that moment employing smoke in the hopes of destroying them'.[42]

Banks seems also to have interested himself in Lee's nursery business. In 1779 he received a long letter from John Lloyd writing from Hafodunos in North Wales. In it, among other items of news, Lloyd gave an account of his visit to Mrs. Egerton at Oulton in Cheshire 'who is very fond of Botany and very deep in it too' and who had made a neat Herbarium of English plants. He continues, 'Lee, her Father's old Friend, has played his cards ill; for when Mr. Egerton was making a new Garden and Shrubbery, Mrs. Egerton recommended him and Mr. Egerton wrote four or five letters, but our friend Lee never answered one of them. I dare say it is 100 £ pr an. at least out of his way, for Mr. E. has made great improvements. He lays out his whole income (17,00£ pr. an) on his own Estate in improvements and never goes to London'.[43]

One would hardly expect a man of Banks's importance to concern himself about a nurseryman's lost order, but in his reply to Lloyd, Banks writes:

'Why would you not apply to me at first about Mr. Egerton. Lee would then have had his custom which I much wish if you see him again offer me as a pledge for Lee's good behaviour and say that I will help his Garden if he will still employ Lee'. This last was a considerable bribe for no one in the country would have more opportunities for obtaining rare plants than Banks.[44]

Lee's advice seems to have been sought when gardeners were needed. James Blaikie, a Scotsman who had collected plants for Doctors Fothergill and Pitcairn in the Alps in 1775, and had probably been employed by the former at Upton previously, kept a diary which was published in 1931 as *Diary of a Scotch Gardener at the French Court*.[45]
He writes:

Friday September 13, 1776. Received a letter from Mr. Lee with one inclosed from Comte De Lauraguais, Mr. Lee having engaged me to go to France the Comtes letter was to the same purport informing me to gett trees from Mr. Lee as he expected a little vesselle of his from France which was to carry the whole to his seat in Normandy. Spent the time in going to Kew and different other places and likewise at Upton until the 30 of Sept. Went to Hammersmith and began taking up plants for Comte Lauraguais. All of my clothes and every thing being ready and packed of. . .
Tuesday the 5 Obre. sent the plants to Waping to be Shipped abord of the Poly Jones. . . .

A few years later Blaikie visited England. 'Spent untill the 4 November Amongst my old acquaintances at Upton, Kew and Hammersmith and about the Country procuring the trees and plants but most of them at Mr. Lees and Hairses. Agreed with Archibald Macmaster to go as gardener to Comte Lauraguais'.

Again in 1785 he returned and recorded 'Went and saw the differant Gardens about London, Mr. Lee who still continues much the same... After spending about a fortnight about London hired a Gardener for the Comte Lauraguais at Mr. Lees this is a young simple Scotsman named Brough.'

Again in 1786 he writes:

'At this time the Duke [of Orleans] desired me to bring him over a Gardener for Raincy. I wrote to my old friend Mr. Hoe* but he declined living his place with the Duke of Northumberland; after I addressed to Mr. Lee who sent me over one who had occuppied a little place at Acton; however as the place was not difficulte he only haveing the Mowing and few Orange trees however he was installed, but seemed rather disatffied but greedy of gain although nothing of a breilant geneus'.

In December 1790 he came back on another visit '...as this was not the Season to See the Gardens so we had little oppertunitty to examin there progress, however went and saw Mr. Lee whose colection is still augmenting and many new plants introduced to his colection; he is Still healthy and hearty.'

William Aiton, of Kew, another Scotsman, must also have known James Lee well and was probably his friend. Lee gave him help with *Hortus Kewensis* and as visitors so often included both Kew and Hammersmith in the same excursion they must have heard a good deal of each other. Unfortunately little is known of William Aiton's personal life, his letters having been destroyed after his death,[46] so that his exact relations with James Lee are not known. In 1776 Lee wrote to Linnaeus 'I am charged by my friend Francis Masson to send you the inclosed specimen & description of a plant that he has found in the Island of Madeira. He is disirous that you would name it *Aitonia* in honour of his friend & patron Mr. Aiton Botanick Gardiner at Kew.' At that time it would seem, therefore, that they were not close friends – Aiton however lived another seventeen years and died two years before Lee.

* Thomas Hoy, gardener at Syon and a member of the first Council of the [Royal] Horticultural Society.

Samuel Gray, as has already been mentioned, is said to have been another friend. James Lee certainly knew his brother Edward Whittaker Gray of the British Museum who gave him some bulbs of *Amaryllis reticulata*, a Brazilian plant he had obtained from Portugal, in 1772.[47] Samuel Gray, as seedsman and importer of roots, would have been likely to be in contact with James Lee, nurseryman.

Thornton says the eminent botanists of the day 'courted' Lee's company and in addition to Philip Miller and Dr. Fothergill he names the Rev. Dr. Hales, Professor Martyn, Dr. Withering, the Rev. Colin Milne and John Hunter. He also says Lee dined once every week with the Marchioness of Rockingham at Hillingdon.[48]

The passage from the autobiography of Fabricius already quoted links Lee with many of the scientists of his day; Fabricius, too, mentions Fothergill and John Hunter (as well as his brother William); possibly Dr. Hales, Professor Martyn, Dr. Withering and the Rev. Colin Milne were included in the 'many others' he does not name.

Stephen Hales – physiologist and inventor – was Minister at Teddington; his most important work was *Vegetable Statics* published in 1727; he died aged eighty-four when James Lee was forty-six so that it seems more likely that James Lee would have 'courted' him rather than the other way round.[49]

Professor John Martyn was Professor of Botany at Cambridge and a correspondent of Linnaeus – for most of his life he lived in Chelsea and died there in 1768. It is possible, therefore, that James Lee knew him. Thomas Martyn, his son, was also Professor of Botany at Cambridge and mentions Lee's 'Introduction to Botany' in his book *The Language of Botany* as containing 'a full explanation of Linnean terms' and as having reached its fourth edition by 1788; the tone of the reference does not suggest that he knew him personally, however.[50]

William Withering was a younger man, having been born in 1741; he was physician, botanist and mineralogist. For most of his life he practised in Stafford and Birmingham. In his *Botanical arrangement of British Plants* he puts Lee's 'Introduction to Botany' among the books 'those who wish to know the curious facts which gave birth to this celebrated system [of Linnaeus] may consult'.[51]

48

The Rev. Colin Milne, a Scotsman born in Aberdeen about 1743, besides being a clergyman at Deptford was a Fellow of the Linnean Society, the author of a *Botanical Dictionary* published in 1770 and of other botanical works; he began, but did not finish, a translation of the *Genera Plantarum* of Linnaeus; he died in 1815.[52]

John Hunter, like James Lee, a Scotsman, was the greatest surgeon of his age. In 1764 he purchased two acres of land at Earl's Court and built there a small country house and a menagerie for his animals. He had a very varied collection which included jackals, zebras, buffaloes and leopards, as well as more domesticated animals and birds and fish.[53] He was interested in the vegetable kingdom as well.

In 1793 Thomas Baird[54] noted 'Mr. Hunter's experiments in regard to the vegetation of trees it would be improper to anticipate... He is very curious in plants, and has, in the green houses and hothouses, a great variety of the most choice and rare productions of nature in the collection of which he has spared neither pains nor expence'. John Hunter was not only a fellow countryman of James Lee but a neighbour, and it is likely that if he purchased his plants from a nursery garden he would have patronized the Hammersmith Nursery. Both men enjoyed the friendship of Sir Joseph Banks and it is probable that they were acquainted.

The Marchioness of Rockingham[55] was the wife (and after 1782 the widow) of the Rockingham who was Prime Minister in 1765 and 1782. The daughter of Thomas Bright, she was a very wealthy woman and indulged in the fashionable hobby of collecting rare plants for her garden. She was responsible for introducing some new species into England.[56] When she entertained the younger Linnaeus in 1781 James Lee and Solander (then Banks's librarian) were present. The note sent by James Lee making the arrangements reads 'Mr. Lee's compliments to Mr. Linnaeus, and begs to know what day Mr. Linnaeus will come to dine with Mr. L at the Vineyard and go to the Marquis of Rockingham and if Dr. Solander can come with him, Wensday will be a very Convenient Day for Mr. Lee if it is equaly so to Mr. Linnaeus, Mr. Lee will order a person to call at Sir Joseph Banks tomorrow for Mr. Linnaeus's answer.

Vineyard, 23 July 1781'.[57]

49

It hardly seems likely that Lee would have dined with the Marchioness *every* week, however. Hillingdon is some distance from Hammersmith.

James Lee obviously took a keen interest in the many voyages of discovery made during his lifetime. Governor Phillip, in his account of his voyage to Botany Bay made in 1789, referred his readers to the 'nursery gardens of the eminent and learned botanist Mr. Lee at Hammersmith' for plants which had been brought from Botany Bay because he had not space to describe them. He says Mr. Lee 'still retains enough zest for his favourite science to regret that the discovery of those countries was not made at a period of his life when he could have gone personally to reap the glorious harvest they afford'.[58] Mr. Lee was then seventy-four.

There is a story James Lee intended to publish a work on the flora and fauna of Australia and sent out Thomas Watling to make drawings for it. This cannot be correct, however, as Watling, whose drawings were used by several early writers on Australia, was sent to New South Wales as a convict for forgery.[59]

On at least one occasion Lee showed his interest in a practical way. Archibald Menzies, surgeon and naturalist to Vancouver's expedition to the South Seas which left England in 1791 wrote in his Journal on March 4 1792 'James Lee of Hammersmith, a gentleman whose liberal and philanthropic mind has ever been arduously engaged in diffusing as well as collecting the vegetable productions of various climes, was so good as to send after me to Portsmouth, a large assortment of garden seeds to be distributed in the course of the voyage wherever they were most likely to be most useful and beneficial to mankind. In compliance with his humane intention I made up a suitable collection of these for Kualelo* before he went on shore with instructions how to manage them and about 150 orange seedlings with some vines that were reared in the frame on the quarter deck'.[60]

James Lee was always ready to befriend and help young gardeners and botanists – especially if they came from

---

* A native of Hawaii who was being returned to his home after having been to Britain.

Scotland. James Dickson, one of the founders of the Royal Horticultural Society, nurseryman and authority on flowerless plants, owed much to Lee's help and encouragement when a young man.[61]

CHAPTER SIX

John Kennedy

IN January, 1782, Lewis Kennedy died and his son John became Lee's partner. John Kennedy was born at the Hammersmith Nursery on October 30, 1759. He was the son of his father's first wife. He also married twice. His first wife was Margaret Hart whom he married in 1781, and she was the mother of twelve of his children. She died in 1801. The children were: Margaret, born 1782 who married John Thomas Pocock; Mary, born 1783; Anne, born September 1784 who married Henry Charles Andrews; Charlotte, born 1786 who married Thomas Bean; a son John who died in infancy in 1788; Lewis who was born in 1789 and became a land steward; William, born 1790, who married and died in America; John who died May 1794 aged two years; Amelia Emily who married William Bridgewater Page; John Henry, born 1795; James, born 1797; and Henry, born 1799, who died when he was twelve years old.[1]

Two of John Kennedy's daughters by his first wife therefore married men who became well known in the botanical world – Henry Andrews and Bridgewater Page.

Henry Andrews is described on the title-page of his *Botanist's Repository* as 'Botanical printer and engraver, etc'. *The Botanist's Repository* was issued monthly in one hundred and thirty-seven numbers between 1797 and 1814. It was intended to rival Curtis's *Botanical Magazine*, which had begun in 1790; it boasted that it contained 'coloured engravings of new and rare plants only'. Curtis gave his work the subtitle the 'Flower garden displayed' and illustrated many well-known garden plants. Curtis's *Botanical Magazine* is still being published, having been taken over by the Royal Horticultural Society, and it maintains today the tradition of fine coloured botanical illustration which Curtis began; it is the oldest journal of its kind in the world.

John Kennedy wrote the descriptions to most, if not all, the plates in the first five volumes of his son-in-law's work and of the 359 plants pictured mention of Messrs. Lee & Kennedy either as having introduced or cultivated the plants is made for 157. Volume 6 published in 1804 has descriptions by Haworth;[2] as has been noted Haworth[3] had no friendly feelings towards the Hammersmith Nursery; from then until the tenth and final volume, published in 1814, no mention at all is made of the Hammersmith Nursery. Plates 659 and 663 of Volume 10 are 'Refulgent-flowered lobelia' 'raised from Botany Bay seed at the Hammersmith Nursery' and 'Self-coloured lily' drawn from a plant at Messrs. Lee & Kennedy. The last plate of all is 664.

Andrews's contemporaries thought little of his botanical knowledge but today his publications are much valued by collectors for their illustrations. In the magnificent volume *Great Flower Books, 1700–1900,* by Sacheverill Sitwell and Wilfred Blunt, reference is made to him as one of the 'minor flower painters. . . who are able to sustain a wonderful temperature of interest throughout a monotonous subject – such as Henry C. Andrews in his monograph on the Ericas with its three hundred hand-coloured plates and his two huge volumes on the South African Geraniums'.[4] In addition he was responsible for *Roses, The Heathery* and other volumes which fetch high prices in the sale rooms.

Henry Andrews lived at various addresses in Knightsbridge.[5] Whether he first met his future wife when he came to make paintings of flowers at Hammersmith, or, whether he came there to paint because he intended to marry her, is not known.

William Bridgewater Page, who married Amelia Emily Kennedy, was employed at the Hammersmith Nursery before going to Southampton where the work which bears his name was produced; it was published in London in 1817.

The title page reads:

Page's Prodromus; or a general nomenclature of all the plants indigenous and exotic cultivated by him in the Southampton Botanic Gardens; arranged alphabetically, as they are considered hardy or tender to the climate of Britain under their different characters of trees, shrubs, herbaceous, etc. . .

Page describes himself as 'William Bridgewater Page, Southampton (from the Hammersmith Nursery) Nurseryman, seedsman and florist (by special appointment) to Prince Leopold and Princess Charlotte'. Princess Charlotte was the only child of the Prince Regent who afterwards became King George IV; her husband was afterwards King of the Belgians. She died the year that 'Page's Prodromus' was published.

John Kennedy is considered to be the author of this book which is mainly a catalogue of cultivated plants; James Britten regarded it as 'a very good one'.[6] Among the heaths listed one notes 'Mr. Kennedy's' and 'Mr. Lee's' and among the gooseberries 'Lee's Princess of Orange' and 'Lee's Princess Royal'.

John Kennedy's second wife was Ann Taylor Reynolds and by her he had nine children; Thomas born 1808; Francis born 1810 and Josephine born May 1811 – no doubt named after his patron the Empress Josephine of France; Henry; Margaret; Francis; Margaret and Jeanet, twins; and lastly Charles. In all John Kennedy had twenty-one children – but only eight of them lived to have children of their own. A delightful portrait of the family painted by Henry Andrews in 1833 shows no fewer than twenty-eight members gathered together.[7]

In addition to writing botanical works John Kennedy was one of those called in by the Empress Josephine to advise her on her garden at Malmaison. He may have been recommended by Redouté who would have come to know him in London in 1789. William Paul in his book *The rose garden* published in 1848 says:

But it was fashion which paved the way for its [the rose's] general reception in France. At the commencement of the present century, the Empress Josephine acknowledged it as her favourite and caused varieties to be collected throughout Europe and brought to her garden at Malmaison. The late Mr. Kennedy was provided with a passport to go and come as he pleased during the war, in order that he might superintend the formation of that garden.[8]

Les Roses by Redouté forms a magnificent monument to the Empress's roses; equally magnificent volumes are those by her botanist Ventenat on the *Jardin de Malmaison*, illustrated by Redouté. In this work a number of acknowledgments are made to 'M. Kennedy, célèbre cultivateur' of Hammersmith, after whom Ventenat named a genus of Australian plants *Kennedia*.[9]

Enormous quantities of plants were shipped to the Empress from the Vineyard Nursery. The *Gentleman's Magazine* of November 14, 1811, notes:

'Curious plants to the amount of £700 value have lately been shipped at Portsmouth for the ci-devant Empress Josephine. They are the produce of a nursery garden at Hammersmith from which she also got a supply in 1803 to the amount of £2,600.'

From France, Kennedy introduced the standard rose tree into England in 1818 and the Duke of Clarence is said to have purchased a thousand standard rose trees at a guinea a piece from Lee & Kennedy.[10] John Kennedy also brought back some of the new fancy pelargoniums, or geraniums, as most of us still call them, from Malmaison and so helped to start a new fashion in greenhouse plants.[11]

Georgette Du Crest in her *Memoirs of the Empress Josephine* published anonymously in 1828 gives a lady-in-waiting's view of the gardens at Malmaison:

When the weather was fine, the green-houses were inspected; the same walk was taken every day, on the way to that spot the same subjects were talked over; the conversation generally turned upon botany, upon her Majesty's taste for that *interesting* science, her wonderful memory which enabled her to name every plant; in short, the same phrases were generally repeated over and over again, and at the same time, circumstances well calculated to render those promenades exceedingly tedious and fatiguing. I no sooner stepped onto that delightful walk, which I had so much admired when I first saw it, than I was seized with an immoderate fit of yawning.[12]

John Kennedy sold his share in the Vineyard Nursery, which by that time included grounds in Kensington, Feltham, Stanwell and Bedfont, as well as in Hammersmith and Fulham, in 1818[13] and went to live in Eltham, Kent, where he died on February 18, 1842.[14]

The Kennedys and the Lees continued to be on friendly terms; Arthur Kennedy (great grandson of John Kennedy and, like his father Thomas, a lawyer) made the will of John Lee, the second James Lee's son by his second wife, in 1888, and John Lee's granddaughter remembers knowing 'the Kennedy girls' when she was a young girl.

CHAPTER SEVEN

James Lee's children: His death

SOMETIME during the 1740s the first James Lee, the joint founder of the Vineyard Nursery, married. Perhaps it was this which made him decide to open a nursery business of his own, instead of remaining as gardener on other men's estates. Little is known of his wife except her name; no record of their marriage has been traced.[1] All that is known of her is the record in the Parish Register of St. Paul's Hammersmith of the burial of Martha Lee, wife of James Lee, nurseryman, on December 24, 1779, age sixty-nine. Thornton says she was a 'kind and most affectionate wife'.[2] They had four children, Susannah born in 1748, Ann in 1753, James in 1754, and lastly Mary.[3] James Lee's only son James inherited his share of the Nursery, but his favourite among his children wash is daughter Ann. There is a family tradition that she was small and dark. She was an artist of considerable talent, who painted flowers, birds and insects and who enjoyed a high reputation in her own time,[4] but, because none of her paintings has ever been published, she is less remembered than she deserves to be. She was a pupil of Sydney Parkinson and also it is said, of Thomas Worlidge.

Sydney Parkinson, a woollen-draper by trade, was an artist by inclination 'taking a particular delight in drawing flowers, fruit and other objects of natural history he became so great a proficient in that stile of painting as to attach the notice of the most celebrated botanists and connoisseurs in that study'.[5]

James Lee was a close friend of his and recommended him to Sir Joseph Banks[6] who employed him to make drawings at Kew and then, in 1768, to accompany him as natural-history

56

draughtman at a salary of £80 a year on a voyage round the world in *The Endeavour* under Captain Cook. On board he made numerous drawings for Banks, 955 in all, and far more than Banks had anticipated – collected various curiosities at the ports of call and kept a journal. Unfortunately he caught fever at Batavia and died on January 26, 1771, while the ship was in the Indian Ocean. Thirty-eight of the ninety-five on board died during the voyage.

When Banks returned home in July, Sydney's brother Stanfield demanded all Sydney Parkinson's effects. Banks handed over everything except some rough sheets of Sydney's journal which, just before he died, he had asked should be given to James Lee. It was James Lee who had suggested that he should write down everything he saw, but, as Dr. Fothergill wrote, 'Could poor Sydney have forseen that he was furnishing avarice and malevolence with the means of traducing such men [as Banks] he would have swerved from the instructions of his cordial and intelligent friend [James Lee] who desired him to "minute everything he saw and trust nothing to his memory". Stanfield, 'an unlettered man' put an inflated value on the journal and accused Banks of holding back other things belonging to his brother, including a silver watch!

Because he had been a friend of Sydney's Dr. Fothergill wrote to Banks on Stanfield's behalf although he was not, at that time, acquainted with Banks. In reply he received a most cordial letter saying that £151 8s. 1d. was due to Sydney Parkinson's heirs with some additional sum for 'such clothes etc. of his as I could dispose of, or make use of, in the ship which I chose rather to do, than bring them home liable to be damaged, as those which came home were in some degree' and that he, Banks, would be most grateful for 'the good offices of some disinterested person' to decide how much should be paid to the executors of Sydney Parkinson's estate – he would like to be generous and show to Parkinson's relatives the gratitude he would have shown to him had he lived.

Dr. Fothergill suggested that the sum of £500 should be paid and that Banks should have the right not only to all Sydney Parkinson's drawings, which were his because they had been made while in his employ, but also to anything he might wish to have from the collection of curiosities Parkinson

57

had made. These terms were very generous and Stanfield agreed to them; he then asked if he might be allowed to see his brother's papers. Banks, knowing Stanfield to be both greedy and ignorant, was rather doubtful about allowing him to borrow them but on his agreeing to make no improper use of them and on Dr. Fothergill promising they should be returned, he allowed him to have them.

The next thing Banks, Fothergill and Lee learnt was that Stanfield Parkinson was in fact having the papers prepared for publication. James Lee wrote an angry letter:

To Stanfield Parkinson

Sir,

I have heard of your unaccountable behaviour to my good friend Doctor Fothergill relative to your intending to publish your brother's papers, after he had passed his word for your making no improper use of them, contrary to the intention of the lender, for they *was* only lent as a *peice* of indulgence which the doctor begged for you, the use you intend to make of this indulgence in my opinion carrys with it the colour of an action so fraught with ingratitude and matchless impudence that should you proceed in it, you will bring a lasting stain on your name and family, and may be followed by the ruin of both.

I little thought that a brother of my late worthy friend Sidney Parkinson, could even thought of such a piece of Treachry it makes me shudder at your vicious turn of mind, while I lemante ever having had any knowledge of a man of such wretched principles. I advise you to desist, and take sham on you before it is *to* late, and that you will for the sake of your family save your reputation which once lost is seldom to be recovered.

One thing more I must tell you which perhaps you think I did not know, which is that in your brother's will, that he left with his sister before he went abroad, he left some legacys to my daughter Ann, amongst other things some paintings that was in your hands. I have likewise heard that there was something left to me in the will Mr. Banks brought home. You have taken no notice of these things to me, I imputed your scilence to your avarice, and did not think it worth my while to disturb you about it but since I have heard of your determination I must tell you if you proceed further in your publication I am determined to call you to an account, the papers you are about to publish is by right mine, I have Mr. Banks word for it that your brother left them to me and I will dispute your title to them as I have witness's of your brothers leaving em to me as my property. Consider the contents of this letter and act like a man of honour or consider the consequences of doing wrong.

I am etc.

Vineyard 26 Nov. 1772.   JAMES LEE

The whereabouts of the original of this letter is not known and it is copied from the version given by Stanfield Parkinson to his editor which appeared in the Preface to his brother's 'Journal'. It may perhaps have been mis-copied because of the splutterings of James Lee's angry pen or by intention. It shows Lee was a man of his time in the individuality of his spelling.

Stanfield Parkinson's long letter in reply attempting to justify his actions contains one interesting passage where he quotes from his brother's will.

'Thirdly I desire that my paintings on vellum etc. may be given to those for whom they are marked on the back, and whatever utensils that are useful in painting or drawing to Mr. Lee's daughter, my scholar'.

Stanfield says he has sent Mr. Lee the 'utensils' and if any paintings 'had been marked for thy daughter she would, of course have had them with the utensils'.[7]

Ann Lee was about eighteen at this time and her finest paintings were yet to be done. Perhaps she used her teacher's 'utensils' for them; some of his paintings have been kept by her family with hers to this day nearly two hundred years later.

Meanwhile Dr. Fothergill was doing his best to get the papers back – Stanfield demanded £500 for 'expenses' incurred in preparing the manuscript for publication. Dr. Fothergill not unnaturally refused to be blackmailed. Stanfield then went ahead and published the volume, including as a preface his version of the quarrel with Banks, the letter from James Lee and his reply to it. Stanfield was not a man of sufficient education to write the preface or edit the book himself but he entrusted the task to Dr. Kendrick.[8] William Kendrick was 'a Miscellaneous writer of considerable ability but whose Writings are contaminated by a style vituperative and malignant' according to his contemporary Watt.[9] *The Dictionary of National Biography* says he, 'became the enemy of every decent and successful person and so notorious as a libeller that few condescended to answer him'. Among those he attacked were Samuel Johnson, Oliver Goldsmith and David Garrick, so Banks, Fothergill and Lee were in good company! The preface contained 'falsehood, misrepresentations and abuse' in Dr. Fothergill's words 'the production of a venal pen and of a writer who has had very little regard to either truth or character'. By this time Stanfield had become insane and was in St. Luke's Hospital, where he died. His family being left destitute, Dr. Fothergill purchased the unsold copies of the 'Journal' and added to them his 'Explanatory Remarks' and this formed the edition published about 1777.

Many of Sydney Parkinson's drawings are in the Botany Library of the British Museum (Natural History); 318 of them were published in 1905 as *Illustrations of Australian plants collected in 1770 during Capt. Cook's voyage round the world*, and some are in the possession of James Lee's descendants.

Thomas Worlidge, the engraver, if he was Ann Lee's teacher,[10] would seem to have been a rather unsuitable one for a child – she was only thirteen at the time of his death. Three times married (his first wife was the daughter of Alexander Grimaldi), the father of thirty-two children of whom only one survived him, 'hot-tempered, habitually employing strong language, gluttonous and often drunk . . . careless in dress. . . a martyr to gout'.[11] His only qualification would seem to be that he lived for part of his time in a house in the Nursery grounds.

Those of Ann Lee's paintings which have survived are exquisitely drawn and coloured and give minute attention to detail so that, for example, every tiny hair of a saxifrage stands out distinct and separate yet the flowers and their leaves achieve an air of being alive which is so conspicuously lacking in the reproductions in some much sought-after flower books. With birds she is a little less successful, perhaps because she drew them dead, instead of from fresh living specimens as she did with flowers. The insects in her paintings often showing several together, seem alive enough to fly or crawl from the pages and among the few animal portraits she did is one of a delightful gnu.

Sixteen of her paintings on vellum of *Mesembryanthemum* are in the Botany Library of the British Museum (Natural History); they were made between 1776 and 1778 and each is signed 'A. Lee'. With the collection are three on paper by Simon Taylor. A hundred of her paintings of flowers are in the possession of her family – they were made between 1767 when she was sixteen and 1779; there are also eighty-five of birds and animals and insects. Some are signed 'Ann Lee', some 'A. Lee', some 'A. L.' and some are unsigned.

She was one of the artists employed by Dr. Fothergill 'to make drawings on vellum when each plant was in the perfection of bloom. He kept three or four such artists constantly occupied and the paintings which he obtained, it is said, two thousand in number, were purchased after his death [in 1780] by the Empress Catherine II of Russia for £2,300'.[12] Among the flowers Ann Lee painted for him was *Arethusa Bulbosa* in 1778.

The other artists Dr. Fothergill employed were Ehret, Taylor, Harris and John Miller – all acknowledged as among the finest botanical illustrators of their day.

At least one of Ann Lee's drawings was in the possession of the Marquis of Blandford when Sir James Edward Smith wrote his *Exotic Botany* published in 1804 – he refers to her as 'late, amiable and accomplished'.[13] Some of her drawings her father sent to Linnaeus. One went with a letter in October, 1772, because James Lee considered Linnaeus had been led to misname a plant through having only examined an imperfect example. His daughter's drawing of a perfect specimen would enable the description and name to be corrected. In October, 1775, he sent another drawing of a new plant 'exactly delineated' which he suggested Linnaeus should name in honour of Miss Blackburne. The following year he tells Linnaeus that he has raised new specimens of *Mesembryanthemum* which his daughter has drawn and offers to lend him the drawings.[14] Those now in the British Museum (Natural History) were made between 1776 and 1778 so some may be the drawings referred to. Ann's ability to draw so accurately must have been a great asset to her father – and his friends. In 1789 L'Heritier de Brutelle wrote to urge Banks to get Miss Lee or Sowerby to make a drawing of *Geranium Spinosum* which Lee had said was in flower.[15]

James Lee inspired Ann 'with a love of his own pursuits, and [she] added to her intimate knowledge of them an exquisite taste in drawing both plants, shells and insects'.[16] She was the daughter 'on whom he doated'.[17] We know that she had a collection of insects because Lady Ann Monson left her her collection of Bengal insects.[18] No paintings by her dated later than 1779 are known and it may be that at that time her eyes began to feel the strain of ten years of such detailed work or that her health began to fail.

Fabricius wrote of her in 1782; she is, he says 'uncommonly gifted at painting and is now the best natural history painter in England. . . She specialises in painting plants, insects, shells and other similar objects of nature. We saw some of her work which has a masterly touch about it'.[19] From this it would seem she was still painting them although he might perhaps have seen paintings done earlier.

She died at Hammersmith in 1790 aged thirty-seven. She was the only one of her father's children who did not marry and, sharing his interests as she did, she must have been his constant companion after the death of his wife. It is hardly surprising that he should feel her loss deeply. In his will he left the sum of £20 to Sarah Stedman, his servant, who may have kept house for him, but who could hardly have taken his daughter's place. His son James had lived at 2 Vales Buildings (on the south side of the main road opposite the Nursery) since about 1783.[20]

Ann's elder sister Susannah was the eldest child; she married Mr. Burton, a silversmith.[21] A family named Burton had been prominent property owners in Hammersmith since the fifteenth century but it is not known whether he was of this family. Susannah died in 1788 aged forty and was buried in Hammersmith.[22] A David Burton was collecting plants in New South Wales in 1791-2 for Lee and Kennedy and others[23] and it is possible that he was her son, or of her husband's family. 'He was a very deserving gardener sent to Port Jackson several years ago by Sir Joseph Banks who after he had there made a ample collection of seeds, with many useful observations relative to their culture was too soon for us called to botanize in the coelestial regions' wrote R. A. Salisbury[24] in 1806. In fact Burton died in Australia as the result of a gunshot wound sustained when duck shooting in April 1792.[25]

The youngest child was Mary, who married a Mr. Crespell and by 1795 had a daughter Susan. Her father left her £50 in his will and Susan £25. She seems to have been less well off than others of her family – perhaps she was widowed early – and in a codicil to his will, made in 1824, her brother James left her the 'annual sum of £30 which I have heretofore paid her' to be paid out of the profits of the business, £15 at Midsummer and £15 at Christmas.[26] Crespell is an unusual name and a James Crespel, a working silversmith, appears in Holden's 'Triennial Directory' for 1802-4 – it is possible therefore that two of James Lee's daughters married silversmiths.

James Lee died on July 25, 1795, and was buried on July 30, at Hammersmith; there is no record of the whereabouts of his grave. His son James was to be buried in Sir Ralph Box's vault in the chancel floor of the old St. Paul's Church.[27] (Sir Ralph Box, a Master of the Grocers' Company, died in 1693.) It may be that James Lee the elder was buried there also. The Box vault disappeared when the old church was pulled down in 1883, but a tablet on the wall of the present church commemorates James Lee the younger and his wife Sarah Eliza.

In his will, made just fifteen days before his death, he left his granddaughter Ann Lee all his 'Fossells, Shells, Insects, Drawings and other things relating to Natural History' – at that time she was six years old; perhaps he hoped she would share her Aunt Ann's tastes. As has been mentioned he left legacies to his daughter Mary, to his other granddaughter Susan and to Sarah Stedman; everything else went to his son James. 'I give devise and bequeath unto my son James all my copyhold Messuages Lands Tenements and Estate and all my Leasehold Estates whatsoever and wheresoever and also all the rest and residue of my Goods Chattles personal Estate and Effects. . . not by me otherwise disposed of'. The will was witnessed by John Kennedy, his partner, and Edward Day.[28]

Among his personal property, inherited by James, was the sword made by Andrea Ferrara which he had brought from Scotland with him; his portrait in oils, showing him holding a flower in his hand, painted by an unknown artist, his magnifying-glass and a set of buttons, each one a tiny painted view of part of the grounds of an estate which it has not, so far, been possible to identify.[29]

James Lee died full of years and honour. 'He was distinguished for a mind replete with benevolence, in his friendships he was steady and warm, in his dealings he manifested the greatest punctuality and integrity and he lived to reap the reward naturally consequent on such qualities in the accumulation of a comfortable independence'. So concludes his obituary in The *Gentleman's Magazine*.[30]

His son James was forty-one when he inherited his father's share of the Nursery. During the next twenty-nine years he was to become sole owner and to extend it to heights of prosperity previously unknown and to hand it on to his children who kept it until the 1890s.

NOTES

WHERE sources are referred to by abbreviated titles only, full details will be found by reference to the bibliography.

CHAPTER ONE

1. Thackeray *Vanity Fair*, Chapter 4, 'for a kiss from such a dear creature as Amelia I would purchase all Mr. Lee's conservatories out of hand'.
2. Loudon 'Encyclopaedia', p. 1224.
3. *Gent. Mag.* 65 (1795).
4. Craig-Brown 'Selkirkshire', Vol. 2, Chapter 9.
5. *Gent. Mag.* 65 (1795).
6. Lee. 1810.
7. Information from Registrar-General's Office, Edinburgh.
8. Information from Mr. J. Roberts, of Selkirk.
9. Craig-Brown 'Selkirkshire,' Vol. 1, Chapter II.
10. ibid., Vol. 2, Chapter 9.
11. ibid., Vol. 2, Chapters 8 and 9.
12. Loudon 'Encyclopaedia', p. 280.
13. This sword is still in the possession of his descendants.
14. Loudon 'Arboretum'.
15. Lee. 1810.
16. Ironside 'Twickenham', p. 109.
17. Bate *And so to make a city here.*
18. Lee. 1810.
19. Letter quoted in full, pages 18-9.
20. Bate *And so to make a city here.*
21. Aiton *Hortus Kewensis*, 1789–99.
22. Loudon 'Arboretum'.
23. Loudon 'Encyclopaedia'.
24. Britten and Boulger 'Biographical Index'.
25. D.T.C. 10(2), 157–8.
26. Lee. 1765.
27. Linnaeus. *Species Plantarum*, ed. Stearn, p. 77.
28. Loudon 'Arboretum'.
29. Information from Miss G. M. A. Beck, archivist at Petworth House.
30. Information from Mr. H. S. Pocock, who is descended from Margaret, grand-daughter of Lewis Kennedy.
31. Loudon—Dr. Jackson in D.N.B. says Kennedy worked for 'Lord Bolton' at Chiswick. No such person can be traced as having a connection with Chiswick during this period, whereas Lord Burlington owned Chiswick House. I am indebted to the Librarian of Chiswick Public Library for help on this point. Mr. T. S. Wragg, Keeper of the Records of the Duke of Devonshire, into whose family the Chiswick property came after the death of Lord Burlington, has not been able to supply confirmation, however.

32. Lee. 1810.
33. Details of Kennedy family from Mr. H. S. Pocock and parish registers of St. Paul's Church, Hammersmith.

CHAPTER TWO

1. Bowack, J. 'Middlesex'.
2. Walpoole, G. A. *The new British traveller*, p. 282.
3. Spencer, N. *The complete English traveller*, p. 315.
4. L.C.C. Survey, p. 13.
5. Charity Commission Report No. 9.
6. Copy of the Admission of James Lee, the younger, 1818, in Hammersmith Public Library.
7. Latymer's will quoted in Wheatley 'History of Edward Latymer' p. 67.
8. Charity Commission Report No. 9.
9. Copy of the Admission of James Lee, 1818.
10. Historical Manuscripts Commission, Report XV, Appendix II, p. 260.
11. Transcriptions of the Manorial Rolls of the Manor of Fulham in Hammersmith Public Library.
12. ibid.
13. ibid.
14. ibid.
15. ibid.
16. Middlesex Land Registry 1818. 5/701.
17. Faulkner 'Hammersmith'.
18. Minute books of The Brentford Turnpike Trust.
19. L.C.C. Survey, p. 10.
20. ibid. p. 15.
21. *Survey of Hammersmith 1829*. In 1823 the Charity Commissioners had described the Edmonton Charity property in possession of the Lees as 'A dwelling-house, with green-house, and other buildings and 4A. 1R. 2P. of land, used as a nursery ground'.
22. I am indebted to Miss Miles for the search of the Manorial Rolls.
23. This copy of Faulkner's 'Fulham' is in the Hammersmith Public Library. No rate books for Hammersmith are known for before 1795.
24. Hyams *Vineyards in England* and Samuel Pegge 'Of the introduction, progress, state and condition of the vine in Britain', in *Archaeologia*, 1.1770.
25. Quoted in Vispré *Dissertation on the growth of Wine in England*, 1786 as from Hales *Compleat Treatise of practical husbandry*.
26. Dack 'Thomas Worlidge'.
27. 'Poor and Church rate . . . accounts', in Fulham Public Library.
28. Westminster Commissioners of Sewers Presentments, 386, 1818 and 390, 1821.
29. W.C.S. Records. Plan 268.
30. ibid.
31. Miller 'Dictionary'.
32. Baird 'General view'.

CHAPTER THREE

1. Smith, J. E. *The English flora*, p. xi.
2. *J. Bot., Lond.* 1.374 (1872).
3. ibid. 53.112 (1915).
4. *Bot. Rep.* Plate 179.
5. *J. Bot., Lond.* 53.112 (1915).

6. This edition is recorded by Dr. B. D. Jackson in *Guide to the literature of Botany* but he seems not to have seen the 1799 edition, a copy of which is in Hammersmith Public Library.

7. Lee. 1810.

8. *Edinburgh Review* 1807.

9. *Gent. Mag.* 65 (1795).

10. Smith Papers, Vol. 3.

11. Blunt *The art of botanical illustration*, p. 207.

12. These letters are in the possession of the Linnean Society of London to whom I am indebted for permission to quote. The letter from Linnaeus to Lee was recently presented to the Linnean Society by James Lee's great-great-grand-daughters. It is in Latin but I have quoted from the English translation which was preserved with it.

13. Mr. R. H. Jeffers in *Gardeners Chronicle* April 16, 1952.

14. Quoted in full, pages 24–25.

CHAPTER FOUR

1. Loudon 'Encyclopaedia', p. 276.

2. ibid p. 1240. A copy of 'Adam armed' is in the Guildhall Library, MSS 3389/2.

3. Switzer *The nobleman, gentleman and gardener's recreation.* p. xviii.

4. Cox *Plant hunting.*

5. Foot 'General view', p. 15.

6. Lysons *Environs of London*, Vol. 2, p. 401.

7. Aiton *Hortus Kewensis* 2nd ed.

8. So described in Watt *Bibliotheca Britannica.*

9. *Bot. Rep.* Plates 7, 16.

10. ibid. Plates 5, 14, 19, 56, 128, 148.

11. ibid. Plates 107, 145, 167.

12. ibid. Plates 22, 68, 87, 100, 127, 212, 280, 341.

13. D.N.B.

14. *Bot. Rep.* Plate 82.

15. R.H.S. *Dictionary of gardening.*

16. *Bot. Rep.* Plates 183, 344.

17. ibid. Plates 35, 59.

18. ibid. Plate 13.

19. Loudon 'Arboretum', p. 78.

20. James Lee, the younger, furnished W. T. Aiton with a list which is included in the List Books at Kew.

21. Fabricius 'Briefe' quoted p. 33.

22. Field 'Memoirs . . . of the Botanical Gardens at Chelsea,' p. 69.

23. *Bot. Rep.* Plates 123, 132, 144, 264.

24. ibid. Plate 189.

25. BM. Add. MS. 8095, 195–196.

26. Bentham Papers Vol. IV. B.M. Add. MS. 33, 540.

27. Pamphlet on the John Shepherd Collection in possession of Liverpool Public Library.

28. Smith Papers, Vol. 3.

29. ibid. Smith wrote in Oct. 1795, from Portland Place, now Addison Bridge Place, 'I . . . now live within 50 yards of Lee's garden (poor old Lee died this summer but his son succeeds him) and I am quite delighted with my house and situation'.

30. Loudon 'Arboretum' p. 78.

31. Wood *A fuchsia survey.*

32. Anderson *The coming of the flowers.*
33. Sitwell *Old fashioned flowers.*
34. Wood *A fuchsia survey.*
35. Anderson *The coming of the flowers.*
36. Blaikie 'Diary'.
37. Faulkner 'Hammersmith'.
38. Salisbury *Paradisus Londinensis.*

CHAPTER FIVE

1. Fabricius. Auto-biography; translated by F. W. Hope *in* Transactions of the Entomological Society of London, 4 (1845).
2. Fabricus 'Briefe'. I am indebted to Mr. F. G. S. Parker for this translation of my transcription of the eighth letter.
3. Thunberg 'Travels', Vol. 3, p. 289.
4. Leger 'Redouté', p. 15.
5. B.M. Add. MS. 8095, 192–193.
6. Information from Miss M. Lee.
7. B.M. Add. MS. 8090, 137.
8. Curtis 'William Curtis'.
9. Smith Papers. Vol. 3, 177.
10. Broadley and Melville 'The beautiful Lady Craven', p. xxx.
11. Jefferson 'Garden book', p. 114–115.
12. Loudon 'Arboretum', p. 139.
13. Smith Papers. Vol. 14, 41.
14. *Bot. Rep.* Plate 255. I am indebted to the Librarian of Winchester Public Library for information about Mr. North who later became the sixth Earl of Guildford.
15. *Curtis's Bot. Mag.* Vol. 2, p. 56.
16. Smith, J. E. *English Flora*, Vol. 1, p. xi.
17. Cruickshank Caricature in the possession of the Royal Horticultural Society.
18. Thunberg 'Travels', Vol. 3, p. 290.
19. Letters in possession of the Linnean Society.
20. Thunberg 'Travels', Vol. 2.
21. *Bot. Rep.* Plate 276.
22. Letter in possession of the Linnean Society.
23. Fox 'Dr. John Fothergill', p. 203.
24. Lettsom 'Memoirs of Dr. Fothergill', p. 39.
25. Fox 'Dr. John Fothergill'.
26. Bartram 'Travels', ed. by Mark Van Doren.
27. *Gent. Mag.* 64.180 (1794).
28. Forster J. R. and G. F. *Characteres generum plantarum.*
29. Letter in possession of the Linnean Society.
30. Hutchinson *A botanist in South Africa.* Pt. 5.
31. *J. Bot., Lond.* 23.227 (1885). The donor was James Lee, son of John Lee.
32. *Hortus Kewensis*, 2nd. ed., Vol. 2, p. 376.
33. Smith, J. E. 'Memoir and correspondence', Vol. 2, p. 117.
34. ibid. p. 183.
35. Cameron 'Sir Joseph Banks'.
36. Esdaile *The British Museum Library*, p. 62.
37. Banks and Solander 'Illustrations of Australian plants'.
38. British Museum. Banks's Correspondence. Vol. 1, Add. mss. 33977.
39. Quoted pp. 46 and 47.
40. Misc. MSS. Royal Society 60, quoted in Cameron 'Sir Joseph Banks'.

41.   Cameron 'Sir Joseph Banks'.

42.   *T.H.S.* Vol. 2, p. 162.

43.   D.T.C. 1, 272–274.

44.   Nat. Libr. Wales, MS. 12415–20.

45.   Blaikie 'Diary'.

46.   Letter from John Smith to James Britten preserved in the collection of Francis Masson's Drawings at the B.M. (Natural History).

47.   *Bot. Rep.* Plate 179.

48.   Lee. 1810.

49.   D.N.B.

50.   Martyn *The Language of Botany*, p. xxiv.

51.   Withering 'Botanical arrangement', p. xv.

52.   D.N.B.

53.   Gray 'Portrait of a surgeon', p. 158.

54.   Baird 'General view', p. 23.

55.   Complete Peerage.

56.   *Hortus Kewensis.* 2nd ed.

57.   Letter in possession of the Linnean Society.

58.   Phillips 'Voyage', p. 294. Mr. James Lee of Hammersmith was among the subscribers to this volume.

59.   Watling's Drawings. British Museum (Natural History) MSS. No. 34, and 'Thomas Watling' by Hugh S. Gladstone *in Transactions of the Dumfriesshire and Galloway Natural History and Antiquarian Society*, 1935–36. 3rd Series Vol. 20, Dumfries, 1938.

60.   Menzies *Hawaii Nei 128 years ago*.

61.   *T.H.S.* Vol. 5, Appendix I.

CHAPTER SIX

1.   Information from the parish Registers of St. Paul's, Hammersmith and Mr. H. S. Pocock.

2.   *J. Bot., Lond.* 42.296 (1904).

3.   ibid. 54. 236–246 (1916).

4.   Sitwell and Blunt 'Great flower books', p. 9.

5.   *J. Bot., Lond.* 54. 236–246 (1916).

6.   ibid. 42. 296 (1904).

7.   Parish Registers of St. Paul's, Hammersmith and Mr. Pocock.

8.   Paul *The Rose Garden*, p. 13.

9.   *J. Bot., Lond.* 42. 296 (1904) and Ventenat *Jardin de la Malmaison*.

10.   *West London Observer*, Jan. 27 1899.

11.   Anderson 'Coming of the flowers', p. 105.

12.   Du Crest 'Memoirs', p. 340.

13.   Memorials of the Middlesex Land Registry 1818. 5. 701.

14.   *J. Bot., Lond.* 42. 296 (1904).

CHAPTER SEVEN

1.   Parish registers of St. Paul's, Hammersmith, and All Souls, Fulham have been checked as well as the nine volumes of 'Middlesex Parish Registers' edited by Phillimore & Gurney.

2.   Lee. 1810.

3.   Parish Registers of St. Paul's, Hammersmith.

4.   Fabricius 'Briefe'.

5.   Preface to Parkinson's 'Journal' [1777].

6.   Introduction by Britten in Banks and Solander, 'Illustrations of Australian plants'.
7.   Parkinson 'Journal' [1777].
8.   *Gent. Mag.* 55 (1785).
9.   Watt *Bibliotheca Britannica.*
10. I am indebted to Mr. R. H. Jeffers for this suggestion.
11. D.N.B.
12. Fox 'Dr. John Fothergill', p. 199.
13. Smith, J. E. *Exotic Botany.*
14. Letter in the possession of the Linnean Society.
15. B.M. Add. MS. 8097, 192.
16. *Gent. Mag.* 65 (1795).
17. ibid.
18. Thunberg 'Travels'.
19. Fabricius 'Briefe'. Translation by Mr. Parker from my transcription.
20. Fulham Highway Rate Book.
21. *Gent. Mag.* 65 (1795).
22. Parish Register of St. Paul's, Hammersmith.
23. *Hortus Kewensis*, 1811, Vol. III.
24. Salisbury *Paradisus Londinensis*, p. 73.
25. Maiden 'Sir Joseph Banks', p. 156.
26. Will of James Lee the younger at Somerset House.
27. Note in an annotated copy of Faulkner's 'Fulham' in possession of Hammersmith Public Libraries.
28. Will of James Lee the elder, in the collection at the Guildhall Library.
29. All these (with the exception of the magnifying-glass, which was stolen) are in possession of James Lee's great-great grand-daughters.
30. *Gent. Mag.* 65 (1795).

UNPUBLISHED SOURCES

Brentford Turnpike Trust Minute Books, 1738–1769, at Chiswick Public Library.
British Museum Manuscript Department.
  Letters from James Lee, the elder, to Sir Joseph Banks and others.
  Letters to and from Banks.
British Museum (Natural History) Botany Library
  Ann Lee's Drawings.
  Francis Masson's Drawings.
  Sir Joseph Banks Correspondence; transcribed by the daughters of Dawson Turner (D.T.C.).
  Watling's Drawings.
Drawings of Ann Lee and others in possession of Lady Wilson.
Kew. Royal Botanic Gardens
  List books, 1793–1809.
Linnean Society of London
  Letters from James Lee to Linnaeus.
  Smith Papers.
  Letter in Sir J. E. Smith's copy of Lee's 'Introduction to Botany', 1810.
  Letter from Linnaeus to James Lee.
Manorial Rolls of the Manor of Fulham
  The original documents are in the Public Record Office and The Guildhall Library and in possession of the Church Commissioners. (Transcriptions made by Dr. Moir and Miss Miles are in Hammersmith Public Library.)
Memorials of the Middlesex Land Registry
  Middlesex County Record Office (Index of Vendors 1709–1837 and Rolls 1709–1772, books 1773–1837).
  London County Council Record Office (Copy memorials 1709–1890) Index of Vendors 1838–1938.
Minute books of the Court of Assistants of the Company of Gardeners, 1764–1800, at The Guildhall Library.
Parish Registers of St. Paul's Church, Hammersmith and All Souls Church, Fulham.
Poor and Church Rate books for Fulham and Fulham Highway Rate book at Fulham Public Library.

Registrar General of Scotland
   Records of births in Selkirkshire.
Survey of Hammersmith, 1829, in possession of Hammersmith
      Borough Council.
Westminster Commissioners of Sewers records in the London
      County Council Record Office.
Will of James Lee, the elder, in the Guildhall Library.
Will of James Lee, the younger, in Somerset House.

PRINCIPAL PERIODICALS CONSULTED

Botanist's Repository (Bot. Rep.).
Curtis's Botanical Magazine (Curtis's Bot. Mag.).
Gardeners Chronicle (Gdnrs. Chron.).
Gentleman's Magazine (Gent. Mag.).
Journal of Botany, British and foreign, London (J. Bot., Lond.).
Notes and Queries (N. & Q.).
Transactions of the [Royal] Horticultural Society of London (T.H.S.).

BOOKS

Aiton, William
   Hortus Kewensis, 3 vols. 1789–99.
Aiton, William
   Hortus Kewensis. 2nd ed. revised by W. T. Aiton. 5 vols.
      Longman and others. 1810–13.
Anderson, A. W.
   The coming of the flowers. Williams and Norgate. 1950.
Baird, Thomas
   General view of the agriculture of Middlesex . . . drawn up for the
      consideration of the Board of Agriculture. 1793.
Banks, Sir Joseph
   The Banks letters; a calendar of the Manuscript correspondence edited by
      Warren R. Dawson. Brit. Mus. (Natural History). 1959.
Banks, Sir Joseph
   Catalogus Bibliothecae historico-naturalis. 5 vols. 1796–1800 (Vol.
      3 *Botanici* 1797).
Banks, Sir Joseph
   Journal during Captain Cook's first voyage in H.M.S. Endeavour *in*
      1768–71; edited by Sir Joseph D. Hooker. Macmillan.
      1896.
Banks, Sir Joseph and Solander, Daniel
   Illustrations of Australian plants collected in 1770 during Captain
      Cook's Voyage round the world. . . with determinations by James
      Britten. 3 vols. British Museum 1905.
Bartram, William
   Travels, edited by Mark Van Doren. Constable. 1958.
Bate, G. E.
   And so to make a city here. Hounslow, Thomasons. 1948.

Blaikie, James
  Diary of a Scotch Gardener at the French Court at the end of the eighteenth century; edited by Francis Birrell. Routledge. 1937.
Blunt, Wilfred
  The art of botanical illustration. Collins. 1950.
Bowack, John
  The antiquities of Middlesex. 1705.
Britten, James and Boulger, George
  A biographical index of deceased British and Irish botanists. 2nd ed. Taylor & Francis. 1931.
Broadley, A. M. and Melville, Lewis *eds.*
  The beautiful Lady Craven: the original memoirs of Elizabeth Baroness Craven, afterwards Margravine of Anspach and Bayreuth and Princess Berkeley of the Holy Roman Empire. 2 vols. Lane. 1914.
Cameron, Hector Charles
  Sir Joseph Banks: the Autocrat of the philosophers. Batchworth Press. 1952.
Cecil, Mrs. Evelyn (Hon. Alicia Amherst)
  A history of gardening in England. Murray. 1910.
Charity Commissioners
  Report No. 9. 1823.
Cockayne, George Edward
  Complete Peerage, edited by V. Gibbs and others. 13 vols. St. Catherine Press. 1910–53.
Coloured specimens to illustrate the natural history of butterflies from the collection of Mr. Lee, Hammersmith. William Miller. 1806.
Cox, E. H. M.
  Plant hunting in China. Collins. 1945.
Craig-Brown, T.
  History of Selkirkshire. 2 vols. D. Douglas. 1886.
Curtis, W. Hugh
  William Curtis, 1746–1799. Winchester, Warren & Son. 1941.
Dack, Charles
  Sketch of the life of Thomas Worlidge. Peterborough Nat. Hist. Soc. 1901.
Dictionary of National Biography (D.N.B.).
[Du Crest, Georgette]
  Memoirs of the Empress Josephine with anecdotes of the Courts of Navarre and Malmaison. 2 vols. Henry Colburn. 1828–9.
Esdaile, Arundell
  The British Museum Library. Allen and Unwin. 1946.
Fabricius, J. C.
  Briefe aus London vermischten inhalts.
Fabricius, J. C.
  Entomologia systematica emendata et aucta. 4 vols. 1792–4. 1784.
Faulkner, Thomas
  Historical and topographical account of Fulham. Eggerton and others. 1813.

73

Faulkner, Thomas
  History and antiquities of Hammersmith. Nichols & Son and others.
    1839.
Field, Henry
  *Memoirs—historical and illustrative of the Botanick Garden at Chel-
    sea.* Gilbert. 1820.
Foot, Peter
  *General view of the agriculture of Middlesex . . . drawn up for the
    consideration of the Board of Agriculture.* 1794.
Fox, R. Hingston
  Dr. John Fothergill and his friends. Macmillan. 1919.
Gourlie, Norah
  Linnaeus. Witherby. 1953.
Gray, Ernest A.
  Portrait of a surgeon: a biography of John Hunter. Hale. 1952.
Hadfield, Miles
  Gardening in Britain. Hutchinson. 1960.
Haworth, Adrian Hardy
  Observations on the genus Mesembryanthemum. 2 vols. 1794–5.
Hutchinson, John
  A botanist in Southern Africa. Gawthorn. 1946.
Hyams, Edward
  Vineyards in England. Faber. 1953.
Ironside, Edward
  History and antiquities of Twickenham. 1797.
Jackson, Benjamin Daydon
  Guide to the literature of botany. Longmans. 1881.
Jefferson, Thomas
  Garden book, 1766–1824; annotated by Edwin Morris Betts. Ameri-
    can Philosophical Society. 1944.
Johnson, George W.
  A history of English gardening. Baldwin & Cradock, etc.
    1829.
Lee, James
  Catalogue of plants and seeds sold by Kennedy and Lee. 1774.
Lee, James
  An Introduction to botany. J. & R. Tonson. 1760.
Lee, James
  An Introduction to botany. J. & R. Tonson. 1765.
Lee, James
  An Introduction to botany. 3rd ed. J. F. & C. Rivington and
    others. 1776.
Lee, James
  An Introduction to botany. 4th ed. J. F. & C. Rivington. 1788.
Lee, James
  An Introduction to botany. 5th ed. S. Crowder and others. 1794.
Lee, James
  An Introduction to botany. 6th ed. improved and enlarged. Edin-
    burgh. James Symington. 1796.

Lee, James
  An Introduction to botany. New Edition. Edinburgh. Wm. Creech and others. 1799.
Lee, James
  An Introduction to botany. New edition corrected and revised by C. Stewart. Edinburgh. Mundell and others. 1806.
Lee, James
  An Introduction to the science of botany, 4th ed. (sic). F. C. & J. Rivington and others. 1810. Contains 'Sketch of the life and writings of the late James Lee' by Robert John Thornton.
Leger, C.
  Redouté et son temps. Paris. Editions de la Galerie Charpentier. 1945.
Lettsom, John Coakley
  Memoirs of John Fothergill. 4th ed. 1786.
Linnaeus, Carl
  Species Plantarum, a facsimile of the first edition 1753. With an introduction by W. T. Stearn. 2 vols. Ray Society. 1957–8.
Linnean Society of London
  Catalogue of the manuscripts in the Library, Pt. I, Smith papers.
London County Council
  Survey of London. Vol. 6. The Parish of Hammersmith. L.C.C. 1915.
Loudon, John Claudius
  Arboretum et fruticetum Britannicum. 8 vols. 1838.
Loudon, John Claudius
  Encyclopaedia of gardening. Longman & others. 1822.
Lysons, Daniel
  Environs of London. Vol. 2 The County of Middlesex. 1795.
Maiden, J. H.
  Sir Joseph Banks. Sydney. William Applegate Gullick. 1909.
Martyn, Thomas
  The language of botany. 1793
Masson, Francis
  Stapeliae novae. 2 vols. 1796–7.
Menzies, Archibald
  Hawaii Nei 128 years ago. Honolulu. 1920.
Merrill, Elmer Drew
  The botany of Cook's Voyages. U.S.A. Chronica Botanica Company. 1954.
Miller, Philip
  Gardener's dictionary. 7th ed. 1759.
Page, William Bridgewater
  Page's prodnomus. T. Cope. 1817.
Parkinson, Sydney
  A journal of a voyage to the South Seas, with explanatory remarks by Dr. Fothergill. [1777?].
Paul, William
  The rose garden. Sherwood and others. 1848.

Phillimore, W. P. W. and Gurney, Thomas, *eds.*
  Middlesex parish registers. 9 vols.
Phillip, Arthur
  The voyage of Governor Phillip to Botany Bay. 1789.
Pulteney, Richard
  Historical and biographical sketches of the progress of botany in England.
    2 vols. 1790.
Royal Horticultural Society
  Dictionary of gardening. 4 vols. & supplement. O.U.P. 1951–56.
Salisbury, Richard Anthony
  Paradisus Londinensis. William Hooker. 1806.
Sitwell, Sacheverell
  Old fashioned flowers. Country Life. 1939.
Sitwell, Sacheverell and Blunt, Wilfrid
  Great flower books, 1700–1900. Collins. 1956.
Smith, Sir James Edward
  The English flora. 4 vols. 2nd ed. Longman, Rees. 1828–30.
Smith, Sir James Edward
  Exotic botany. 2 vols. R. Taylor. 1804.
Smith, Sir James Edward
  Memoir and correspondence edited by Lady Smith. 2 vols.
    Longmans and others. 1832.
Spencer, Nathaniel
  The complete English traveller. 1772.
Switzer, Stephen
  The nobleman, gentleman and gardener's recreation. 1715.
Thunberg, Charles Peter
  Travels in Europe, Africa and Asia. 3 vols. 1779.
Todd, H. M.
  Vine growing in England. Chatto. 1911.
Ventenat, E. P.
  Jardin de La Malmaison. 2 vols. De l'Imprimerie de Grapelet.
    1803–4.
Vispré, Frances Xavier
  Dissertation on the growth of wine in England. 1786.
Walpoole, George Augustus
  The new British traveller. [1770?].
Ward, N. B.
  On the growth of plants in closely glazed cases. John van Voorst.
    1842.
Watt, Robert
  Bibliotheca Britannica. 4 vols. Constable and others. 1824.
Wheatley, William
  History of Edward Latymer and his foundations, revised edition.
    Latymer Upper School 1953.
Withering, William
  A botanical arrangement of British plants. 3 vols. 2nd ed. 1787–92.
Wood, W. P.
  A fuchsia survey. Williams & Norgate. 1950.

APPENDIX

List of plants first introduced into England, or first cultivated by Lee and Kennedy during the lifetime of James Lee, extracted from the second edition of *Hortus Kewensis*.

Latin name	English name	Country of origin
	1753	
Alstroemeria Pelegrina (2:303)	Spotted-flower'd Alstroemeria	Peru
	1756	
Euonymus atropurpurens (2:29)	Purple-flower'd Spindle-tree	North America
	1760	
Rudbeckia fulgida (5:131)	Small hairy Rudbeckia	North America
	1765	
Crataegus elliptica (3:201)	Oval-leaved Hawthorn	North America
Crataegus pyrifolia (3:200) [= C. Calpodendron]	Pear-leaved Hawthorn	North America
Silphium connatum (5:163)	Round-stalk'd Silphium	North America
Silphium therebinthinaceum (5:163)	Broad-leaved Silphium	North America
Spiraea lobata (3:257) [=Filipendula rubra]	Palmated Spiraea	Siberia
	1766	
Fagus ferruginea (5:298) [=F. grandifolia]	American Beech Tree	North America
Juglans angustifolia (5:296) [= Carya illinaënsis]	Narrow-leaved Walnut Tree	North America

77

Latin name	English name	Country of origin
	1769	
Ranunculus parnassifolius (3:352)	Parnassia-leaved Crowfoot	South Europe
Ranunculus platanifolius (3:354)	Plane-tree-leaved Crowfoot	Alps of Germany & Italy
Sempervivum Sediforme (3:173) [= *Sedum nicaeense*]	Stonecrop-leaved Houseleek	South Europe
	1772	
Ephedra monostachya (5:417) [= *E. procera*]	Small Shrubby Horse-tail	Siberia
	1773	
Aristotelia Macqui (3:144)	Shining-leaved Aristotelia	Chili
Caladium bicolor (5:311)	Two-colour'd Caladium	Cultivated in Madeira
Prunus nigra (3:198)	Black Cherry Tree	Canada
Prunus pensylvanica (3:198)	Upright Pennsylvanian Cherry Tree	North America
Rosa pumila (3:263) [= *R. gallica* var.]	Dwarf Austrian Rose	Austria & Italy
	1774	
Acacia tamarindifolia (5:473)	Tamarind-leaved Acacia	West Indies
Allium Chamae-moly (2:240) [= *A. chamaemoly*]	Bastard garlick, Dwarf Moly.	Italy & Spain
Andromeda ferruginea (3:52) [= *Lyonia ferruginea*]	Rusty-leaved Andromeda	North America
Annona glabra (3:335)	Smooth-fruited Custard-Apple	Carolina
Buddlea globosa (1:250) [*Buddleja globosa*]	Round-headed Buddlea	Chili
Copaifera officinalis (3:60)	Balsam of Capevi	South America
Elaeocarpus serratus (3:301)	Saw-leaved Elaeocarpus	East Indies
Empetrum album (5:336)	White-berried Heath or Portugal Crake-berry	Portugal
Erica triflora (2:386)	Three flower'd Heath	Cape of Good Hope
Gleditschia horrida (5:475) [= *G. sinensis*]	Strong-spined Acacia	China

78

Latin name	English name	Country of origin
Hypericum Ascyron (4:422)	Siberian Tustsan or St. John's Wort	Siberia & the Pyrenees
Sedum virens (3:114) [= *S. rupestre*]	Green Stone-crop	Portugal

1775

Casuarina stricta (5:232) [= *C. quadrivalvis*]	Upright Casuarina	New South Wales
Cistus scabrosus (3:308) [= *Halimium alyssoides*]	Rough Cistus	Italy & Portugal
Erica tubiflora (2:372) [= *E. curviflora*]	Tube-flower'd Heath	Cape of Good Hope
Pelargonium glaucum (4:170)	Spear-leaved Crane's-bill	Cape of Good Hope
Pelargonium scabrum (4:179)	Rough wedge-leaved Crane's-bill	Cape of Good Hope

1776

Brosimum Alicastrum (5:477)	Jamaica Bread Nut tree	Jamaica
Erinus fragrans (4:49) [Probably *Sutera lychnidea* and *Zaluzianskya capensis*]	Dark-flower'd Erinus	Cape of Good Hope
Lygeum spartum (1:135)	Rush-leaved Lygeum	Spain

1777

Alyssum alpestre (4:95)	Italian Madwort	Italy
Aster diffusus (5:63) [= *A. lateriflorus*]	α. Red-flower'd diffuse Star-wort β. White-flower'd diffuse Star-wort	North America
Avena sibirica (1:170) [= *Stipa sibirica*]	Siberian Oat-grass	Siberia
Leea aequata (2:50) [= *L. sambucina*]	Shrubby Leea	East Indies
Pelargonium glutinosum (4:176)	Clammy Crane's-bill	Cape of Good Hope
Primula marginata (1:309)	Silver-edged Primula	Alps of Switzerland
Zamia debilis (5:410)	Long-leaved Zamia	West Indies

79

Latin name	English name	Country of origin
	1778	
Aethionema monospermum (4:80)	One-seeded Aethionema	Spain
Geoffroya inermis (4:322)	Smooth Geoffroya, Bastard Cabbage-tree	Jamaica
Hieracium undulatum (4:455)	Wave-leaved Hawkweed	Spain
Ixia crateroides (1:89) [= *I. speciosa*]	Crimson Ixia	Cape of Good Hope
Rhammus alnifolius (2:17) [= *R. alnifolia*]	Alder-leav'd Rhammus	North America
Solanum stramonifolium (1:403)	Broad-leaved Nightshade	West Indies
Terminalia catappa (5:441)	Broad-leaved Terminalia	East Indies
	1779	
Convolvulus sibiricus (1:328) [= *Ipomoea sibirica*]	Siberian Bind-weed	Siberia
Nepeta botryoides (3:381) [= *Schizonepeta annua*]	Annual Siberian Catmint	Siberia
Passiflora glauca (4:152) [= *P. arborea*]	Glaucous-leaved Passion-flower	Cayenne
Veronica incisa (1:28) [= *V. linariifolia*]	Cut-leaved Speedwell	Siberia
	1780	
Albuca altissima (2:249)	Tall Albuca	Cape of Good Hope
Cistus formosus (3:306) [= *Halimium lasianthus*]	Beautiful Cistus	Portugal
Pelargonium tricuspidatum (4:179) [Horticultural hybrid— parentage not known]	Three-pointed Crane's-bill	Cape of Good Hope
Salix hastata (5:354)	Halbert-leaved Willow	Switzerland & Lapland
	1781	
Schwenkia americana (1:1)	Guinea Schwen-kia	Guinea
	1782	
Erica umbellata (2:365) [= *E. australis*]	Umbell'd Heath	Portugal

Latin name	English name	Country of origin
Iberis violacea (4:85)	Blunt-leaved purple Candy-tuft	—

1784

Biscutella sempervirens (4:77)	Downy-leaved Buckler-mustard	Spain
Carthamus salicifolius (4:492) [= *Carlina salicifolia*]	Willow-leaved Carthamus	Madeira

1785

Linaria origanifolia (4:15)	Marjoram-leaved Toad-flax	South Europe

1786

Pelargonium heterogamum (4:172)	Six-stamen'd Crane's-bill	—

1788

Banksia oblongifolia (1:216)	Oblong-leaved Banksia	New South Wales
Banksia serrata (1:218)	Saw-leaved Banksia	New South Wales
Begonia humilis (5:285)	Small Begonia	West Indies
Fabricia laevigata (3:183) [= *Leptospermum laevigatum*]	Smooth-leaved Fabricia	New South Wales
Gladiolus floribundus (1:101)	Large-flower'd Corn-flag	Cape of Good Hope
Lambertia formosa (1:211)	Red-flower'd Lambertia	New South Wales
Melaleuca armillaris (4:413)	Pale-flower'd Melaleuca	New South Wales

1789

Echium argenteum (1:300) [= *Lobostemon argenteus*]	Silvery Viper's Bugloss	Cape of Good Hope
Hillia longiflora (2:314) [= *H. parasitica*]	Long-flower'd Hillia	West Indies
Mespilus tanacetifolia (3:206) [= *Crataegus tanacetifolia*]	Tansy-leaved Hawthorn	Greece
Metrosideros hispida (3:183) [= *Angophora cordifolia*]	Rough Metrosideros	New South Wales
Othonna perfoliata (5:178) [= *O. amplexifolia*]	Perfoliate Othonna	Cape of Good Hope
Oxyanthus speciosus (1:371) [= *O. tubiflorus*]	Tube-flower'd Oxyanthus	Sierra Leone

81

Latin name	English name	Country of origin
Senecio haematophyllus (5:38) [= *Gynara haematophylla*]	Purple-leaved Groundsel	—
Serruria pendunculata (1:199) [= *S. artemisiefolia*]	Woolly-headed Serruria	Cape of Good Hope
Zinnia verticillata (5:92) [= *Z. multiflora*]	Whorl-leaved Zinnia	Mexico

1790

Aristea capitata (1:108)	Tallest Aristea	Cape of Good Hope
Crowea saligna (3:36)	Willow-leaved Crowea	New South Wales
Dilatris corymbosa (1:108)	Broad-petal'd Dilatris	Cape of Good Hope
Erica Aitoniana (2:372) [= *E. jasminiflora*]	Aiton's Heath	Cape of Good Hope
Erica canescens (2:406) [= *E. villosa*]	Hoary Heath	Cape of Good Hope
Erica sordida (2:374) [= *E. conspicua*]	Sordid Heath	Cape of Good Hope
Grevillea buxifolia (1:206)	Box-leaved Grevillea	New South Wales
Grevillea serica (1:204)	Silky Grevillea	New South Wales
Ixia columellaris (1:88)	Variegated Ixia	Cape of Good Hope
Leucopogon lanceolatus (1:323)	Small-flower'd Leucopogon	New South Wales
Myginda uragoga (1:282)	Saw-leaved Myginda	South America
Polypodium asplenifolium (5:505)	Spleen-wort-leaved Polypody	Martinico
Primula nivalis (1:308)	Snowy Primrose	Dauria
Pterospermum acerifolium (4:194)	Maple-leaved Pterospermum	East Indies
Piper nigrum (1:69)	Black pepper	East Indies

1791

Gladiolus Watsonius (1:96)	Watson's Corn-flag	Cape of Good Hope
Hakea saligna (1:210)	Willow-leaved Hakea	New Holland
Podolobium trilobatum (3:9) [= *Oxylobium trilobatum*]	Common Podolobium	New South Wales
Lasiopetalum ferrugineum (2:36)	Rusty Lasiopetalum	New South Wales

82

Latin name	English name	Country of origin
Styphelia viridiflora (1:322) [= *S. viridis*]	Green-flower'd Styphelia	New South Wales
Westringia rosmariniformis (3:372)	Rosemary-leaved Westringia	New South Wales

1792

Bossiaea heterophylla (4:267)	Various-leaved Bossiaea	New South Wales
Bossiaea Scolopendrium (4:267) [= *B. scholopendria*]	Flat-stemm'd Bossiaea	New South Wales
Daviesia ulicina (3:20)	Furze-leaved Daviesia	New South Wales
Malva divaricata (4:215) [= *Spaeralcea sp.*]	Straddling-Branch'd Mallow	Cape of Good Hope
Mirbelia reticulata (3:21) [= *M. rubiaefolia*]	Reticulated Mirbelia	New South Wales
Moraea edulis (1:112)	Long-leaved Moraea	Cape of Good Hope
Passiflora aurantia (4:153)	Orange Passion-flower	New Caledonia & Norfolk Island
Sowerbaea juncea (2:231)	Rush-leaved Sowerbaea	New South Wales

1793

Aster tomentosus (5:47) [= *Olearia tomentosa*]	Tooth-leaved Star-wort	New South Wales
Bignonia australis (7:34) [= *Tecoma australis*]	New South Wales Trumpet-flower	New South Wales
Lachnaea eriocephala (2:415)	Woolly-headed Lachnaea	Cape of Good Hope
Mesembryanthemum acutum (3:215) [= *Cephalophyllum subulatoides*]	Great Awl-leaved Fig-marygold	Cape of Good Hope
Mesembryanthemum speciosum (3:250) [= *Drosanthemum speciosum*]	Specious Fig-marygold	Cape of Good Hope
Myoporum debile (4:60)	Procumbent Myoporum	New South Wales
Sprengelia incarnata (1:320)	Flesh-colour'd Sprengelia	New South Wales
Staavia glutinosa (2:35)	Clammy Staavia	Cape of Good Hope

1794

Boronia pinnata (2:349)	Hawthorn-scented Boronia	New South Wales

7

Latin name	English name	Country of origin
Gladiolus versicolor (1:98)	Changeable Corn-flag	Cape of Good Hope
Mesembryanthemum decumbens (3:234)	Decumbent Fig-marygold	Cape of Good Hope
Mesembryanthemum fastigiatum (3:231) [= *Aridaria plenifolia*]	Level-topp'd Fig-marygold	Cape of Good Hope
Mesembryanthemum retroflexum (3:236) [=*Lampranthus elegans*]	Shrubby white-bark'd Fig-marygold	Cape of Good Hope
Pothos macrophylla (1:269) [= *Anthurium grandifolium*]	Large-leaved Pothos	West Indies
Primula cortusoides (1:308)	Cortusa-leaved Primula	Siberia
Struthiola imbricata (1:272) [= *S. striata*]	Tiled leaved Struthiola	Cape of Good Hope
Watsonia brevifolia (1:95)	Short-leaved Watsonia	Cape of Good Hope

1795

Latin name	English name	Country of origin
Atragene capensis (3:342) [= *Anemone capensis*]	Cape Atragene	Cape of Good Hope
Babiana sulphurea (1:105) [= *B. stricta*]	Pale-flower'd Babiana	Cape of Good Hope
Erica costata (2:372) [=*E. versicolor*]	Ribb'd-flower'd Heath	Cape of Good Hope
Helianthus pubescens (5:127) [= *H. doronicoides*]	Downy Sun-flower	North America
Pelargonium elegans (4:167)	Elegant Crane's-bill	Cape of Good Hope

The names added in square brackets above are intended to help the contemporary gardener to identify the plant listed.

Index

NIGHT MUSIC

The night began with the audacious
shooting of shady investigator Al Land.
Now the burden has just been com-
pounded for overworked Detective Frank
Vandegraf and his two colleagues, Jilly
Garvey and Dan Lee. It's only one of a
series of murders to occur across their
city over several hours in an evening.
The already strained resources of the
department can't help them: they're
on their own against the clock, fatigue,
and mounting pressure from above.
And neither victims nor suspects prove
to be quite what they initially seem . . .

TONY GLEESON

NIGHT MUSIC

Complete and Unabridged

LINFORD
Leicester

First published in Great Britain

First Linford Edition
published 2015

Copyright © 2014 by Tony Gleeson
All rights reserved

*A catalogue record for this book is available
from the British Library.*

ISBN 978–1–4448–2627–2

Published by
F. A. Thorpe (Publishing)
Anstey, Leicestershire

1

For a character with such a checkered past, there was surprisingly little of interest to be said about Al Land. He was hardly a taciturn man — by all accounts he was loud, brash, arrogant, and a braggart — but only a few real facts were known about him.

His real name was Albert Landreaux and, like his hometown of New Orleans, he served as a meeting point for all kinds of people from all backgrounds and walks of life. A chosen few intimates knew him well or even beyond the context of why they might find themselves in a room together. Al had served in the Army and then had a short stint as a cop.

According to him, he had decided to take his wisdom and experience to a more profitable arena. According to several members of the force, it was suggested he leave because he was an undisciplined lout and general problem.

For whatever reason, he had bid the department farewell, obtained a private investigator's license and founded his own security agency.

The general stock in trade of the real-life PI — divorces and skip-traces — was hardly beneath him, but he also worked for high-profile clients of all varieties: corporate security, industrial espionage, personal bodyguard, security consultant, and a range of dubious services for the fringes of the legal profession. Very little was publicly known about most of this.

Al was a conspicuous spender and favored expensive three-piece suits and all the accoutrements. He had been fortunate in finding his soul mate in his wife and business partner Anita, a tight-lipped, firm-jawed woman with dishwater-blonde hair and a nasty attitude. Few people could tell you the color of her eyes since she always wore heavy dark-rimmed sunglasses.

They ran their small agency and their lives together in a free-wheeling, tough and irreverent manner, and kept their own counsel.

Needless to say they had nurtured their fair share of grudges, resentments and enmities. All very privately. So what happened that night, some thought, was perhaps inevitable.

Somewhere around ten o'clock on the night of Thursday the twelfth, Al and Anita were sitting in Al's favorite bar, Saint Expedito, near the waterfront. Saint Expedito is the patron saint that New Orleans musicians pray to, to get paid on time, and the bar's owner, Mitch LaRoche, had imported the Cajun music and atmosphere from the hometown he shared with Al.

This particular evening, Al and Anita were the only patrons, sitting at a table near the bar, and discussing the day's business. Al was turned three-quarters towards the door where he had a view of the entryway.

Anita got up to use the ladies' room in the back. Mitch had been swabbing up there and left the bar to go move his mop and bucket. She had no sooner entered the restroom when there came two loud shots from the front.

Mitch turned to look and was whacked in the head by the ladies' room door, which was flying open. As a result, what he saw was patchy: the back of a man in a dark hoodie running towards the door.

Al was slumped backwards over the heavy oak chair. Anita had bolted from the loo, yelling in her hoarse voice. She ran to Al, ascertained almost immediately that he was dead, shot through the head and heart, and sped out of the bar after the assailant.

There were shouts and the sounds of cars starting up, and the squeals of a couple of sets of tires. Mitch called the police.

★   ★   ★

Detective Frank Vandegraf was not very happy at having drawn this case. For one thing, he hated going anywhere near the waterfront. For another, he had known Al Land. For still another, this looked to be one of those cases with nowhere to go and an impossible number of ways to get there.

It was now about two-thirty in the morning. He stood, notebook and pencil in hand, looking over the scene while a handful of uniforms and crime-lab investigators coolly went about their business, deftly avoiding jostling one another in the narrow saloon. The entrance to the bar was wrapped with skeins of neon-yellow police tape.

Al, Frank noted with approval, had not moved since his untimely demise and still reclined backwards over the captain's chair, rusty-colored puddings of congealed blood covering his expensive white shirt and black leather windbreaker.

Sitting nearby were Mitch and Anita, each with a bottle of beer. Anita, in her tinted glasses, was dragging on a well-worried cigarette, understandably distraught but composed. Smoking was illegal now in these establishments, Frank thought, but who was really going to care?

He had to admire her toughness. Quite a broad, he thought sarcastically. You weren't supposed to use that expression anymore, were you? They were constantly reminding him that his attitude was prehistoric.

Anita's voice was deep and tobacco-raspy. 'So Mitch opens up the restroom and he's moving the pail outa the way and I'm no sooner in the stall and pulling down these pants and sitting down than I hear the shots. Damn, these tight jeans, if it had been a few seconds sooner I would have been able to get right out. But I've got to pull these things back up and . . . '

'I got the picture, Anita,' Frank interrupted quietly. He did not particularly care for profane women. Sometimes he really did feel like these just weren't his times any more.

'Yeah, so I was right out the door and there was Al lying back in his seat and this guy running out of the bar; all I can see is he's wearing a dark hoodie, black or maybe blue . . . '

'She swatted me damned good with the door too.' Mitch grinned grimly, rubbing the side of his head. 'She was outa there like a shot.'

'I took a quick look at Al and yelled to Mitch to call for an ambulance. His gun was gone. The scumbag took his gun. Can you believe it?'

'So you say you went after him.'

'Damn right. He had a dirty old piece of junk of a Chevy Blazer right outside and he jumped in and peeled out. Luckily our car was parked right down the street. I took off after him.'

'Not a smart thing to do, Anita.' Frank shook his head, never looking up from his notebook.

'I wasn't exactly thinking straight,' she said and drew savagely on her cigarette and stubbed it out in the ashtray. 'I chased the creep all over but I finally lost him.'

'What did you figure you were going to do if you caught up with him?'

'Bring him in. I've been a bounty hunter, for God's sake, I've brought 'em in. Barring that, plug the SOB.'

There was an awkward silence. Frank just stared. She shrugged. 'Well, I *said* I wasn't thinking straight.'

'So you carry a gun too?'

'Sure. Al and I both do.'

'I'm going to need to see that, Anita.'

She reached under her jacket and pulled out a small revolver, carefully placing it on the table.

7

'I had it out on the seat in case I needed it. Hasn't been fired tonight,' she muttered. 'If that's what you're worried about.'

'Is this your only gun?'

'It sure is. Wanta search me?'

Frank sighed again. 'No, that will not be necessary, thank you. What kind of gun did Al carry? Any chance he was shot with his own weapon?'

'A 9 mm Glock. No way. No way in hell would Al have let a guy like this get close enough to pull his gun. He must have shot him first and then taken it.'

That made sense. Anyway, there were no casings anywhere. Probably a revolver.

'Seems like he did let the guy get close enough to shoot him at close range,' Frank mused. 'Could it have been someone he knew?'

'Sheesh . . . could have been anybody!' Anita shook her head. 'Al *knew* a lot of people and a lot of people *knew* him.' She made the word sound positively nasty.

Frank sighed. Quite the love match all right, these two. He would charitably chalk her demeanor up to her own peculiar form of grief. 'Anybody right now who particularly didn't like him?'

'If you've got an hour to spare,' Anita replied, 'I'll start an enemies list.'

She had no idea who the assailant was and couldn't give any better a description than Mitch had offered. A medium-height fairly lean guy in a dark hoodie — and maybe jeans. The only person who had seen the shooter from the front was Al, and he was of no help just now.

They talked a bit about Al's current well-publicized legal problems. He had been accused of threatening a potential witness in an upcoming case involving his current client.

So in a brief wink of an eye, the killer had come into the bar, fired from a couple of yards into Al, taken his gun, and run out the door.

'If it had just been a minute earlier,' Anita rasped between puffs. She had just seen her husband shot dead in cold blood and taken part in an ill-advised high-speed chase through town, but she was composed and lucid. She was tough, all right. You had to respect that.

'I would have nailed the lowlife. I had just, well, just sat down, if you follow me.'

'Yeah,' Frank nodded, 'I gotcha, you said that. No need to paint me a picture.'

Anita was nonetheless beginning still another description of her travails in the ladies' room, when Frank's cell phone rang. He still carried one of the older models, the kind that folded up, couldn't play films or talk back to him. One of these days he'd enter the new century and pay some exorbitant amount for a big-screen phone.

He gratefully excused himself, stepping away to answer. He curtly barked into the receiver a couple of times then snapped the phone shut, with a head shake.

'All right,' he announced to them both, 'I think I've got everything I need for the moment. I'll most likely be contacting you again. You've each got my card, so please let me know if you can think of anything else.'

'Sounds like you're a popular guy tonight,' Anita said wearily, not looking up at him while searching for another cigarette.

'Some more bodies in a parking lot,' Frank replied over his shoulder. 'Some kind of brawl or something. Nice night.' He looked at the crime scene gang and added, to nobody in particular, 'See you in a while.'

2

Detective Jilly Garvey wasn't delighted either, to be where she found herself just then. She had already been warned that there would be a wait for any coroner or technical people; apparently it was one monster of a night for the city's already-strained thin blue line.

She surveyed the dark side street, about two blocks from the main thoroughfare, lined with quiet inexpensive apartments and an occasional barroom. Two uniformed officers were giving her a tour of the late-model Acura sedan parked curbside, and its ill-fated inhabitants.

Keeled over to her right side in the driver's seat was a young woman with blonde hair and *café-au-lait* skin. She had been very pretty, Jilly thought.

Her eyes were large and brown, fixed open in a final stare of surprise and shock.

She had been shot once in the head at

reasonably close range, perhaps five or six feet. Her bag lay open beside her, with a wallet and other items spilled out over the seat and floor.

Jilly was able to find and read an ID easily enough without disturbing anything else. Her name was Marina Belize. In the passenger's seat, slumped into the corner between the door and the seat back, was a thin dark-complexioned man in a black shirt. He, too, had been shot from the driver's-side window — possibly one shot through the back of his head and throat.

There was not yet any identification as to who he was. The officers did not want to further disturb the scene to look for his wallet until the coroner's van had arrived. Both had been killed, they agreed, in what looked like a drive-by shooting.

Sirens were sounding off in the distance. No doubt some of them at least were headed here. Jilly smirked. A little night music. Her nights were seldom without it.

Just exactly when, she asked herself, did this kind of thing stop getting to me and start becoming just another part of the job? When did the chaos and noise become something I think of as a sound track?

One of the uniforms interrupted her reverie. 'Detective Garvey? Your partner would like a word.'

A few doors away, Detective Dan Lee was trying to calm down a very agitated woman in a long black coat. The woman was crying, cursing, and yelling, in an effort to get past Dan, who looked as if he was attempting to keep her from getting too close to the car.

As Jilly approached, her partner looked up almost plaintively, clearly uncomfortable, while keeping a restraining hand on the woman's shoulder.

He wasn't very good in this kind of situation and no doubt was hoping Jilly would step in and relieve him.

'This is 'Johnny.' Didn't catch her last name,' Dan said in way of introduction. 'She's the deceased's sister.'

The woman was, perhaps, in her mid-thirties, with long jet-black hair. She was jabbering nonstop, without making any particular sense, in English and in another language — it didn't sound like Spanish — possibly Portuguese.

Jilly moved to put her arm around the woman's shoulder. That seemed to calm her slightly. The sound of an orchestra suddenly punctuated the scene and halted her in mid-motion.

'That cell phone of yours.' Dan shook his head. 'What is it with the classical music, anyway?'

'It's *Eine Kleine Nachtsmusik*,' Jilly replied as she reached into her pocket and brought her phone to her ear. Mozart stopped.

The woman's babbling continued, though with less energy.

'A Little Night Music. Personal joke. Hello.' She listened a moment and handed the phone to Dan. 'We got another call. My guess is you'd rather go handle it while I take care of this one.'

Dan had an unmistakable look of relief as he took the phone, his eye still on the unsettled woman. He spoke tersely and handed the phone back to her.

'Yeah. We got a stabbing over on Webley. Give me a call when you're done here.' Without further ado, he fled the scene.

Jilly turned her attention back to the distraught woman who was getting more agitated again. She let loose with a string of what sounded unmistakably like serious non-English cuss words.

'*He's* the one who got her killed, that ... that ...' Another string of foreign oaths, spat out of her mouth viciously. Now Jilly was certain the woman wasn't speaking Spanish. She kept trying, with ever more force, to move past Jilly to get to the car.

Jilly was a fairly tall woman — taller than the younger woman — and that came in handy in situations like this. She placed her hands on the woman's shoulders and held her firmly, looking her in the eye. She tried to speak tough but quietly.

'Okay, look, believe me, you really do not want to go over there. You don't. Now I need you to calm down. I know this is hard but I really have to ask you some things.'

The woman stopped, began to shudder

and sob. She put her face in her hands and began violently shaking. The crying erupted. Jilly let her go.

'Listen,' she said after a minute or so. 'My name's Detective Jill Garvey. You can call me Jilly. I need to talk to you but we can wait a little bit. Take your time and tell me whenever you're ready.'

There was a long pause. She slowly wound down. Jilly waited patiently.

'Can you talk now?' The woman nodded, looking down and wiping her face.

'So your name is Johnny, is that right?'

'It's Jah-*nay*. You spell it Jané but in Brazil you say Jah-nay.'

'And the woman in the car back there is your sister?'

'*Si* — I mean, yes. Marina. Her name is Marina Belize.'

'And you think the man in the car with her is the reason she was shot?'

'He must be. He's no good.' She spat out an unfamiliar epithet. More Portuguese, Jilly assumed. It sounded highly impolite if not downright graphic.

'So who is he?'

17

'His name is Ricky Wright. I don't know why she hangs around with him. He's trash.'

'Why do you think he got her shot?'

'It's one of those other girls he's with. He thinks they don't know about each other. One of them must've gotten wise and come after him and her.'

Jilly pulled out her notebook and started to make some notes.

'So that's Ricky in the car with her?'

'Probably. Tall skinny guy, messy mop of brown hair, thick eyebrows, always wears black?'

'Sounds about right.' Jilly nodded. 'So how did you and she and he happen to all be around here tonight?'

'Marina and I met at the club around the corner. Las Candilejas. We both love to dance, but we don't get to do it much. My husband Eddie's working tonight.

'Ricky was there dancing with a legal secretary he had just picked up. Marina was gonna have it out with him because she had already found out about the dancer he was seeing. Now she sees him with this other girl — so she figures, this

18

is the one, right? — and confronts him.

'He's trying to be all smiley and nice and wants to talk with her privately in her car. He's trying to be real charming, you know? Marina's not real happy about it but she finally agrees and they go outside.

'The secretary is getting all bent out of shape and I'm telling her to butt out of it. We said a few more things back and forth then she pushes past me and goes out the door all mad.'

'How do you know she was a legal secretary?'

'One of her friends at the bar tells me. Three of them, they were all legal secretaries at this law firm. The two girls still in the bar, they were nice enough, trying to make peace with me so I wouldn't go out after their friend, maybe. I wanted to follow Marina and Ricky out to make sure she was okay but they told me it'd be better to let them work it out.

'They said they didn't think their friend would go after them, she wasn't like that, she'd come back in. Now I wish I had gone after them. I started telling them what a bum and a liar Ricky was and we

19

all got to talking for a few minutes. They even offered to buy me a drink.'

'Ricky Wright, huh,' Jilly mused. 'Hardly sounds like she met Mr. Right.'

'Yeah, Marina's a smart girl! Works in a bank, she's got a good career. She could do so much better than that fool!'

'So then what happened?'

'These two gals and I, we had a quick drink together, and we got caught up in just complaining about guys, you know? I suddenly realized Marina wasn't coming back. Their friend didn't come back either. We paid our bills and went out on the street. That's when I heard the sirens.'

'This secretary — what was her name?'

'Lemme think . . . they called her Cat. Catherine, maybe?'

'What'd she look like?'

'Nothing special. Brownish hair, blonde streaks, kinda long and straight. Not all that attractive. But a nice figure, I guess. Dressed nice. Short black dress.'

'Any chance either of the other girls are still around?'

'They were gonna try to find Cat and go home. I don't know. I haven't seen any of them around here.'

It was suddenly momentarily very quiet on the street. Then the crackle of a patrol car radio rang out. Sirens sounded in the distance, some of them at least probably heading here along with, hopefully, the crime scene investigators.

More night music. It was never quiet for long, Jilly thought. The music always turned up again.

She continued to talk with Jané — her last name was Nascimento — for a few more minutes and then told her the best thing she could do was to go home and try to rest.

She gave Jané a card with her contact information then called over one of the uniforms to drive the woman home.

She walked over and scrutinized the car a while longer then decided she'd try the club real quick before moving on to the next show of the evening.

The two secretaries were of course nowhere to be found among the few people scattered outside the club catching air or trying to talk. Las Candilejas was still roiling, oblivious to the excitement less than two blocks away. The salsa music roared in her ears as she entered.

It was a fairly small place, a lot of chrome and dark wood, not much in the way of lighting, a small claustrophobic dance floor.

She shouted questions as best she could above the din, and found the bartender who had served the girls, a young friendly good-looking dark-haired guy.

She showed her badge, motioned him to the side and tried to make herself heard over the night music. At least toward the rear of the bar the noise was muffled a bit.

He remembered the secretaries; they were fairly regular customers. 'They like to dance. And they seem to like us romantic Latin guys, you know?' He said that rather ironically, rolling his big dark eyes and smiling with charming self-effacement, kind of a 'What are you supposed to do?' attitude. Despite herself, Jilly smiled back.

'Did you notice the guy who picked one of them up?'

'Ohhh yeah. You gotta mean Ricky. Yeah, we all know him. I won't tell you some of the names they call him around here. He's so stupid he thinks they're compliments.'

'So he's a regular?'

'He's in here enough that we all know him. Thinks he's a real stud. Brags he's got three, four girls on a string.'

'Do you know any of his supposed girlfriends?'

'There's a nice girl, I think she's Brazilian, she comes in here now and then. Kind of too good for him, you ask me. Smart, looks like she's got a good career. But Ricky's got a certain charm. He's a bad boy, you know?'

'Did you see her here tonight?'

'Actually, yeah. She and a friend, cousin, I dunno. Real cute girls, both of them. She saw Ricky chatting up this other girl, getting like too friendly with her, and she tore into him.

'He was trying to sweet-talk her down. Trouble is, maybe a week ago she found out about Luisa, the red-headed dancer from Tooey's down the street. Not like it was any great secret around here. I think maybe Ricky finally got enough dimes dropped on him.'

'Oh, he got a dime dropped on him,' Jilly mused. 'I'm going to need to talk to you again. You here most nights?'

'Thursday through Sunday. And they always know where to find me. What's going on?'

'Drive-by shooting around the corner. I think it was your nice little Brazilian girl.'

'Ohhh no! No way!'

'Ricky too, it looks like. What else do you know about the red-headed dancer?'

He shrugged. 'Nothin'. Just heard her name. You could check out Tooey's.'

'Did any of the secretaries pay with a credit card tonight?'

'No, they were cash.'

'Any way I might find any of them?'

'Actually . . . ' He walked to the register and sprang it, then returned with a folded cocktail napkin. 'One of them sorta slipped her name and number to me.' He smiled, half-pleased, half-embarrassed.

Jilly jotted down the name, 'Samantha Covington,' in her notebook.

The bartender watched as she wrote it down. 'So they're both — like, dead?'

'Afraid so.'

'¡*Dios mio!*' His expression turned grave. He crossed himself and murmured a prayer in Spanish. All in all, Jilly thought, he was taking it quite well. Conceivably this was not the first patron he had known who wound up dead.

Fifteen minutes later she stepped out of Las Candilejas. It was a welcome change — cooler and quieter.

A little more Mozart. Her phone again.

'What, nobody else is up tonight? Yeah. Yeah. Okay.' Jilly took the info. 'I'll be there as soon as I can,' she sighed and slipped the phone back into her bag. She dialed Dan.

'How's it going over there? Caught another DB. Corner of Parker and San Mateo. Meet me there when you can . . .'

3

The female uniformed cop was young and inexperienced, and it probably hadn't been all that long since she had been set loose by her training officer.

But she was doing her best to be brisk and businesslike.

Frank couldn't help but think that she was afraid that an old Neanderthal like him wouldn't take her seriously.

He didn't believe he was like that, despite the kidding he took from some of his younger colleagues about being a dinosaur, but certainly there were guys in the department who were.

There was a fair amount of blood. The parking lot fronted a 24-hour Ready Rite drug and convenience store that had seen better days. About a dozen witnesses and 'looky-loos' had gathered, and were being held at a distance from the scene.

The coroner and crime-scene personnel had already begun arriving and setting up shop around the bodies. Two other officers were interviewing individuals off to one side.

'This one,' Officer Pardo was saying as she pointed her flashlight at the crumpled guy sprawled on the pavement, 'got hit full-on. No witness accounts of the vehicle involved, but it seems to have hit him pretty hard, then kept going, ran right over him. Maybe it careened against that old Chevy Blazer over there, maybe one or two other cars, and just kept going.'

The man had been crushed beneath the wheels of the vehicle and he lay splattered across the concrete. Even though the night was chilly, he wore only a grey tee shirt over his grimy jeans and work boots.

'He had a wallet and ID. Name's Rudy Caliente. Thirty-nine years old. He was also packing, a cheap five-shot .38. Nobody's quite sure yet if he was involved in the other killings over there.'

She motioned to a second and third body perhaps thirty feet away and began to lead Frank towards them.

'Severin Foster,' she announced, introducing the short dark young man in sweatshirt and jeans, laying on the pavement on his side, arms in a defensive position above what was left of his skull.

'Called 'Sonny' by two of the witnesses. Neighborhood kid. Nineteen years old. Beaten to death with a large blunt metal object, most likely that metal pipe over there or whatever it is.'

'Looks like a piece of rebar,' Frank interjected. The parking lot was home for all manner of trash and castaway objects. Driving around here presented a challenge.

'It's not unusual for these guys to hang out here,' Pardo continued, 'work on their cars, even late at night. Nobody's willing to say what happened or how many people were involved; there was *some* kind of confrontation that degenerated into a brawl.'

Or maybe, thought Frank, could this be premeditated? Did somebody show up here with the definite idea of taking a few people out? It didn't seem likely, but time would tell.

He stepped over to examine the metal rod, rusty brown, with recent smears of dried blood. This piece of junk had been lying in the street for a long time. If you're on a death mission, he considered, would you rely on using whatever instrument of opportunity might be lying around handy on the ground?

'Third victim,' Officer Pardo was continuing, 'Nicholas Lowell. Thirty-two years old. Car salesman.' The unfortunate Mr. Lowell was lying, more or less prone, arms and legs spread, where he had fallen out of his expensive-looking maroon SUV.

His legs still hung from the cab, the driver's-side door halfway open, having closed back on his legs after he fell. It looked like he had been trying to get out of the car, an unsuccessful act made all the more difficult by the fact he had been shot in the left side of the face at extremely close range.

He was wearing another flashy leather jacket, Frank noted, not unlike Al Land's. Beneath it the collar of a light beige shirt was visible. The pants were khakis

— maybe Dockers — and black loafers encased his feet.

'We have not yet ascertained which, if any, of the vehicles in the lot belonged to Caliente and Foster, sir. Nobody will admit to having actually seen what occurred. They all claim to have been inside the store or elsewhere at the time.'

'Sure. Of course they were. Would it be too hopeful to ask if there were any security cameras working?'

Pardo pursed her lips in a sour-lemon expression and shook her head. 'There's only one outside camera on this whole lot, and it's been out of order for a couple of weeks.'

'Thank you, Officer Pardo,' Frank grunted, hands in his coat pockets, surveying the scene around him. He began to pace around slowly, making his way back to the prone figure of Rudy Caliente, who resembled a mannequin made out of hamburger stuffed into a grey tee shirt.

It was a strange coincidence. A dead guy with a .38, who possibly could have been walking back to a white Chevy

Blazer when he was hit. The driver creamed him and then smacked into the truck.

Frank knelt down next to the body, took a pen out of his shirt pocket and carefully slid it into the trigger guard of the pistol lying slightly underneath the body. He edged the gun out from underneath and peered at it.

He walked over to the beat-up Blazer, pulling on a pair of the latex gloves he always carried in his pocket, and opened the driver's-side door.

There was a bunch of trash strewn across the passenger's seat: empty beer cans; a brown-bagged uncapped pint vodka bottle, its contents spilled; a bag from a burger joint with scraps of onions and blobs of ketchup; and a small open cardboard box of .38 shells, a few of them spilled out onto the seat. There was an old-style folding cell phone on the console.

And a dark blue hooded sweatshirt on the floor, with even darker stains that looked a lot like blood.

He opened the glove box. A lot of

miscellaneous junk — and a photocopied registration.

Rudolph Caliente. 3426 Hatchings Avenue. Bingo.

Slightly underneath the front seat, the faint gleam of something made of shiny black leather with a gold metal trim. Frank carefully edged it out with his pen. It was a large billfold-style wallet, stylish and new-looking.

The gold snap had come loose and items were spilling out, including a few credit cards and a driver's license with the picture of an Asian woman, attractive despite a severe expression, with a sort of page-boy haircut not quite to her shoulders. Probably snapped before she was ready: the typically highly flattering portrait from DMV Studios.

Her name was Tia Carlisle. Her address was also 3426 Hastings. Wife? Girlfriend? He happened to notice her birthdate. It was today. Or rather, it had been today until midnight. Now it was yesterday.

Further underneath the seat was something a little more worrisome. There was a hunting knife in a scabbard. The snap was not fastened. It stuck as he tried to slide it out . . . it was caked in brown blood.

In fact, Frank now noticed, there were blood stains all over the passenger's seat. The knife and sheath had been tossed there and had fallen to the floor, probably as the car was driven away.

Frank backed out of the Blazer and yelled, 'Officer Pardo?' She hurried briskly back to him.

'Were any shell casings found around the car salesman?'

'No, sir.'

Frank considered the possibility that Rudy Caliente had shot Al Land in the bar, stabbed somebody else somewhere else and, finally, shot Nicholas Lowell, the car salesman, here in the parking lot. Did he also bludgeon young Sonny Foster to death as well? This seemingly logical solution only presented dozens more questions, starting with: why did Rudy shoot Al Land? — and ending with — who ran over and killed Rudy Caliente? — and, more importantly — why?

Frank continued to stroll around the

scene. No shells — .38 revolver might be right. He walked around Lowell's SUV. It was a nice, almost new, well-kept car, recently detailed. That would figure if the guy sold cars for a living.

There was a fairly deep dent in the front that stood out from the pristine quality of the rest of the car — had to have been done very recently, maybe that very evening. Flecks of paint from the other car still remained. He paused to inspect something else that stood out even more — a bullet hole in the passenger's-side door.

Lowell had been shot from the driver's side. Had somebody taken a shot at him from the other side of the car as well? Was it Rudy? Or had it been somebody else?

Next to Lowell's sprawled face-down body was a carbon-grey, wafer-thin, expensive-looking cell phone with a large screen. A wireless remote earphone was still stuck in his ear, reminding Frank of a character in some science fiction movie he had seen.

Lowell apparently had been in the act of making a call when he was shot. Frank knelt down and carefully picked up the phone in his glove-encased hand.

The person Lowell had been calling was known to him: he had the number on speed dial. The name was still emblazoned on the screen.

'Well I'll be . . . ' Frank muttered.

★　★　★

The young woman lay sprawled in the alleyway on her left side, her right arm stretched out as if still trying to hold off her assailant. Her fur-trimmed suede jacket, white blouse and dark skirt were saturated with large darkened blots of blood. It looked as though she had been stabbed repeatedly. A big caramel-colored leather bag lay a few feet away, its articles spilling all over the pavement around it. The patrol officer and Detective Dan Lee gazed down at the body.

'Looks like a robbery,' the officer was saying. 'And she fought back. No ID on her yet.'

'Who called this in?' Dan asked the officer.

'Somebody on the street, I guess, happened upon her. I was told they wouldn't leave a name. That's not unusual.'

'No it's not. Nobody wants to get involved.'

The alley ran from Webley, a major thoroughfare, to Wesson, a smaller parallel street. She had gotten about halfway down the alley when she was overtaken by her attacker. She could have been coming from either direction but Dan decided it made more sense she was coming from Webley.

Among the items strewn around the ground were an unopened pack of cigarettes, a pack of breath mints . . . and some more personal apothecary items. One door up from the alley on Webley was the 24-7 Market.

'Good chance she was in the quickie mart around the corner,' Dan muttered. 'I'm gonna go talk to them.'

A twenty-something slacker kid was leaning against the snow-cone machine behind the counter. He instantly knew who Dan was and why he was there. He registered what would have to pass for enthusiasm.

'She was in here,' he told Dan. 'Geez, that's awful.'

'So, you were just gonna sit here, weren't gonna come tell us?'

'No, man, nothin' like that. I'm, y'know, not supposed to leave the store. I can get fired for that! I knew you'd find me.'

Dan rolled his eyes, pulled out his notebook. 'So what can you tell me about her?'

'Well, she was in a hurry. Bought a pack of smokes and a couple other things. Personal things?' He snickered. 'Guess she had a hot date. Kinda dressed up. She was kinda hot. For, you know, an older lady.'

Dan marveled that a prodigy like this guy hadn't yet meteorically risen above a minimum-wage counter job. Maybe he was CEO material. 'Was she alone?'

'Yeah. I think somebody dropped her off out front. I'm not sure though.'

'Did you see her leave? Was anybody waiting for her?'

'Nah, don't think so. There was some

noise outside as she finished paying
. . . she just ran out the door. I did kinda,
y' know, check her out as she was leaving.
Kinda interesting, for her age.'

'Yeah. You said that already. Did you
see where she went or anything else?'

'She turned right, towards the alley.
That's about it.'

'Hear anything after that?'

'There's always stuff goin' on out there.
Cars, people yellin', fights, all sorts of
stuff, y' know? I heard somebody peeling
out, some brakes, some shouting, but I
didn't think much about it.'

'So you didn't think anything had
happened until . . . ?'

'Some lady runs in yellin' she needs to
use the phone. She must've been the one
called you guys. I'm not supposed to let
anyone use the phone, y' know? But she
was so nuts and said it was an emergency.
So she calls, hollers into the phone, and
then runs out again all scared. I didn't see
where she went. And then, oh, man, the
sirens. The cops started showin' up.
Coupla black-and-whites with the lights,
man.' He spun a finger in a circle. His

eyes momentarily crossed.

'What'd this second woman look like?'

'Man, I don't remember. She was just yellin' and crazy.'

Great, Dan thought.

'So then you left the store to see what was going on?'

'Well — I just sorta stuck my head out for a minute, yeah. Asked somebody what was goin' on, and they said some chick had gotten stabbed in the alley. Geez, that's awful.'

Dan shook his head. 'Any idea who she is?'

'Well, she paid with a credit card. That oughta help, huh?' The kid opened the register and fished around under the change tray. He pulled out the charge slip and handed it to Dan.

'Yeah,' Dan said, looking at the slip. 'That oughta help.'

★   ★   ★

The corner of Parker and San Mateo was a few blocks off the main drag, neither well-lit nor well-traveled. It was in what was called a 'transitional' neighborhood, mostly transitioning downward. Dan pulled up and had no trouble parking two doors away. Jilly and a lone uniformed officer were the only living souls present.

A third figure lay supine on the pavement, her head slightly resting against the stucco wall of the corner building. She could no longer be counted among the living. She was a middle-aged woman with greying dark hair and a long, shabby dark overcoat.

Dan came closer and bent down to inspect her. She had been shot through the throat and had bled profusely. Probably hit the carotid artery.

Jilly was concentrating on the wall itself. There was a hole at approximately breastbone height — the right size and shape to have been caused by a bullet, and she was prying at it with a small penknife as the uniformed officer looked on. Jilly glanced up and nodded acknowledgment to her partner.

'Not much more to do here,' she said. 'Pretty cut-and-dried it was a drive-by shooting. Not sure who she is. There's no

ID. Felix here says he's seen her around.'

Officer Felix shrugged. 'Once or twice. She's a street person, probably from this neighborhood. I'm not sure if she's got a home or not. That's about all I know.'

'There's some glass on the street out there, and what looks like some fresh rubber burns.' Jilly pointed.

They had hastily erected some yellow tape around the curbside area with a few trash cans they had dragged from down the street. 'Maybe the fool perp shot right through his own car window before peeling out.'

'That would be pretty stupid,' Dan said.

'Well, it doesn't make much sense that someone would execute a drive-by shooting on a neighborhood street lady, either. But that looks like what we got here. Coroner caught up yet?'

'They're back at the quickie mart,' Dan said, yawning. 'Maybe they'll even get here before sunup and we can get out of here.'

'Here's the bullet,' Jilly grunted, suppressing the urge to yawn along with him. 'Aside from that, we haven't got much else.'

'I'm sorry, Detective, but there is absolutely no way I can spare anybody right now.'

Captain Howard Crowley had the look of a man with the weight of the world on his shoulders. The news of eight, apparently unrelated, nocturnal homicides had brought him to the office in the middle of the night and he was not a happy man.

Frank, sitting across the desk from him, was out of any further pleas, arguments, or cajoleries after perhaps ten minutes of doing his exhausted best. The look on the captain's face told him: case closed.

'I don't have to tell you about the caseloads we've all gotten dropped on us recently. And you probably know that this being an election year, we're already getting pressure from above to clear those crimes, and I'm sure you understand that that pressure is going to get lots stronger with this sudden spate of new homicides, especially when the media get to work on them.

'This couldn't have come at a worse moment. We are stretched beyond thin right now. We've had several sickouts from this flu that's been going around. Two detectives are on vacation leave. It's just bad luck.

'Next week I can hopefully get somebody back and assign them to help you out. In the meantime, I'll have to leave it all in your capable hands.'

Frank did not at the moment feel all that capable. His own table had not exactly been clear when the fun had started this past evening.

'Can I at least get some priority on the ballistics or the lab work?'

Another deep sigh from the man in charge. 'I've just had another fight with Morgan in ballistics over this very issue. He's in the middle of a turf war, he says he's got two of his own best people out sick, and he's just about had it. He's adamant that everyone has to wait their turn. I'm sorry, Frank, I can't help you there.

'The medical examiner, blood work, fingerprints, maybe, but I think right now you'd do better trying to persuade them yourself.'

It was pretty bad, Frank reflected, when his people skills were considered the better choice. He resigned himself to what was coming.

'Now, if there's any silver lining on this, it's that I can pretty safely say that this time, I can authorize all the overtime necessary, so your pay check will be getting a significant boost this week.

'Lee and Garvey picked up four homicides tonight as well and when they come in, I'll be telling them the same things I've just told you.

'I'm going to need you all to step up on this. I don't have to tell you, we need to see these cases cleared.'

What did not need to be said was the impending pressure about to come down on the captain from above, which would of course be passed down the line.

Crowley stood up to signify the end of the conversation. 'That's about all, Detective, thank you.'

★ ★ ★

The sun was already coming up when Jilly and Dan returned to the squad room.

A thin crew of three or four were the only others around, and Frank was just leaving. Dark circles under his eyes made him look even wearier than usual, which was saying something.

'Frank, you look like warmed-over road-kill.'

Frank was reminded of the actual human road-kill he had so recently witnessed. 'Caught four homicides tonight. Four.' He wearily held up four fingers.

'Well, what a coincidence,' said Jilly. 'So did we. Where exactly is everybody else tonight? Are we it?'

Frank shrugged. 'Eight deaths in one night! A little of your night music, Jilly?'

'A little,' she grunted. '*Eine Kleine Nachtmusik.*'

'There you go again,' Dan said.

'More like *Eine Kleine Achtmusik*,' Frank said.

'Huh?' asked Dan.

'*Nachtmusik* means 'Night Music,'' Jilly murmured. 'In German.'

'I know that,' said Dan.

''*Acht*' means 'Eight' in German. Frank's making a joke.'

Dan just stared.

'Dan's got no sense of humor,' Frank said, elbowing him in whatever playfulness he could muster. 'You know that. By the way. Just a heads-up. Captain's here.'

He jerked a thumb back to the commander's office. 'He's going to give you the same speech he just gave me. There's no help right now. As you just said, Jilly, we are it.'

'As if we didn't already have plenty to deal with,' Dan said wearily.

'And now, the good news,' Frank said wryly. 'There is going to be authorized overtime, whatever we need. For once it won't be an issue.'

'Lovely,' grumbled Jilly. 'Well, we can all use the money, can't we?'

Frank thought of recent fights, usually not successful, to win even a few hours of overtime to reduce his case load. Be careful, he considered, what you ask for.

'I'm gonna go catch a few hours of sleep and get back on the horse. Probably see you two later this morning.'

After Frank had departed, Dan and Jilly sat down to work out a plan of action and to divide up their tasks.

'Makes sense for me to follow up on the alley stabbing,' Dan said.

Jilly nodded. 'For the moment I'll try to cover the unidentified woman. Not much to be done on that one — maybe some canvassing. But I'm more interested in Marina Belize and Ricky Wright. I think I at least need to start there. There's the possibility of a warm trail that might cool down rapidly.'

Dan nodded. He had a similar feeling about the particulars of his own case. 'You want to take lead on Belize and Wright, then? No problem.'

Dan was one of the junior detectives in the squad, having just made his promotion from patrol only a year earlier. In many ways he felt he was still proving himself, but he also had the self-confidence to take it in his stride.

He had learned that his partner had excellent instincts and organizational skills. Whatever plan she worked out, he could trust it. 'I'll connect up with you later today on Marina and her boyfriend.'

'Some boyfriend,' Jilly snorted, resting her head in her hands. The exhaustion was catching up. 'More like a bad luck charm. How about we follow Frank's lead and clock out for a few hours, then meet back here at, say, nine?'

'How about more like four?' yawned Dan. Jilly shot him a look. 'Just kidding, just kidding. See you at nine.'

For him, that probably meant sleeping in the break room, but it would hardly be the first time.

4

Jilly entered the Goff Boulevard branch of Western Empire Security Bank to find it heavily grief-laden. Marina Belize had been a well-liked and popular manager and the word of her death had spread among the employees and their customers like wildfire.

Handwritten expressions of heartfelt sympathy, little sprays of flowers, and other tokens of bereavement had been left all over the office.

The senior bank manager and other employees were of little help, as Jilly had expected.

Marina lived alone and by all accounts was friendly, intelligent, and helpful. Nobody could suggest a single enemy she might have had. Nobody was at all familiar with Ricky Wright by name or description. Furthermore, nobody seemed able to volunteer a single fact about Marina's family or friends outside of work. Apparently Marina had done a good job of keeping her professional life separated from her personal life.

Marina had purchased a condo in a fairly nice part of town. Jilly couldn't catch a clue there either. There was no building superintendent and many of the neighbors were at work.

There was an elderly couple on Marina's floor who had only encountered her casually, but said she had always been cheerful, polite and helpful. She never even played loud music — 'even though she was, I think, a Latina of some kind,' the wife volunteered then looked embarrassed at having said that aloud.

Jilly resolved to return that evening. Maybe there would be someone who could shed some light on an increasingly murky episode.

* * *

Samantha Covington had answered her cell phone immediately. She was bewildered by Jilly's phone call but willingly gave the address of Byrd, Farmer, Blakey and Silver, the law firm where she worked. The young receptionist's moony eyes opened still wider at Jilly's badge and she quickly picked up the phone, hit a button, and said, 'Sam, there's a police-woman here to see you?'

Jilly took a deep breath, and kept her voice reasonably even. 'Detective, actually.'

Samantha Covington, better known as 'Sam,' was in her late twenties, with short dark hair and wearing expensive-looking designer eyeglasses. She stood and led Jilly back to a vacant conference room where they wouldn't be disturbed.

'Were you in Las Candilejas Thursday night?'

'Sure. I've only been there a few times though. We all had to work a little late and we were, you know, unwinding a little.'

'So you were there with friends?' Jilly consulted her notebook. 'Especially some-one named . . . Catherine?'

'You must mean Kathleen Mueller. 'Kat,' we call her. Yes, I was there with Kat and another girl named Gail. Why?'

'Did Kat meet a man named Ricky Wright there?'

'Oh yeah, I know who that must have been. He was just dancing with her, trying to make time, you know. There was a little problem. Is that what this is about?'

'A problem?'

'Seems that some other girl decided he was *her* boyfriend and started getting real aggressive towards Kat. The other woman was a Latina with a nasty temper. Really got in Kat's face. Kat wasn't happy about that and started giving back some attitude. The guy took the other girl aside and asked her to step outside with him so he could talk to her.'

'And you heard all this while it was going on?'

'Gail and I were at the bar talking to the bartender. Yes, I heard when it started to get ugly.'

'It must have been pretty loud in there. You could hear them arguing over the music?'

'Well, yeah — come to think of it, it must have been a pause between songs, you know? You know how it suddenly gets quiet, and you hear people talking loud over the music? It was like that.'

'So what happened next?'

'Kat was trying to keep this guy with her, and the other girl's got a friend who comes over and tries to get her to stay out of it.'

'Her sister, actually. It was the other girl's sister.'

'Really? She didn't say anything about that. Well . . . Kat just lost it, called her a witch or something like that, shouldered past her and left. I started to go after her to see if I could help, but her friend . . . er, her *sister*, stopped me and asked if I was with Kat. I told her, yeah, we worked together and what business was it of hers?'

'Then what?'

'She was actually okay, but just concerned. We ended up talking and she was telling us about what a jerk this guy was. She said she wished her friend . . . sister . . . would just wise up. We actually had a drink together and started talking about all the losers we had all known.'

'Did Kat or the other girl ever come back into the bar?'

Sam thought for a moment. 'Actually . . . no. Neither one did. We all of a sudden realized we should probably go look for them. We finished our drinks, paid our bills and went outside.'

'And did you find them?'

'Well, Kat was standing right outside the door. She looked a little sick.'

'Any idea where she had gone after she left the bar? Did she say she had followed the other girl?'

'I don't think so. I think she started feeling sick as soon as she was outside. We scooped her up and headed back to Gail's car down the street.'

'And what happened to the other girl?'

'I have no idea. She just walked away, I guess. The guy might have still been trying to talk to her, cool her down. But the last time we saw her was when she left the bar with him.'

'You said she — Kat I mean — looked sick? How do you mean?'

'Like she was going to throw up. I think she'd had a few too many drinks — and she was upset about the argument. We just drove her home.'

'And you and Gail saw her right to her door?'

'Well, yeah, of course we did.'

'I'm going to need to talk to both Gail and Kat.'

'No problem,' said Sam. 'I'll go get them for you. What's this all about?'

'Ongoing investigation,' Jilly said.

The stories told by Kat and then Gail seemed consistent with what Samantha had told her. Kat looked exactly as Jané had described her except, perhaps, a little prettier, but strangely demure — and not at all brassy or loud. Her demeanor outside the festive atmosphere of a dance club was quiet and thoughtful, and she seemed embarrassed by the occurrences that had led up to the tragedy.

To Jilly's trained eye, Kat wasn't the type of woman who carried a pistol as a matter of routine nor, in her judgment, was Kat capable of a carrying out a crime of passion fueled by a man she had met casually in a bar.

What had originally seemed to be a

promising lead — an argument fueled by jealousy erupting in the heat of the moment — suddenly looked anything but promising. Jilly couldn't see how any of these three, normally sedate young women, could have been involved in the shooting outside Las Candilejas, and none of them seemed likely to shed any further light on the event.

It was also evident from their shocked responses that they had not known about the killings before she told them and, she judged, they were genuinely shocked by her news.

Jilly had tried to be discreet, but before her examinations were finished, the word had spread around the office that a police detective was there to investigate some lurid crime or other.

Suddenly, numerous staffers discovered crucially important tasks that required them to walk past the conference room or even to knock on the door to ask a question of one of the women being interviewed.

All the furtive peeks into the conference room annoyed Jilly, but the three women being interrogated actually seemed thrilled by all the attention. Which just confirmed Jilly's gut feeling that she was not on a particularly helpful trail at the moment.

She was disappointed, but somehow also relieved, when she finally wrapped up the conversations and exchanged contact numbers with each witness, in case she had further questions to ask them, or if they had further information for her.

★ ★ ★

'Morgan, please,' Frank persisted, rubbing his eyes as he held the phone to his ear. 'All I'm asking you to do is move a couple of these cases up the line a little. If I can get some results maybe I can clear one or two . . . '

'My heart positively bleeds for you, Detective. The answer is still no.' Lovely man, Morgan. Even the captain, hardly a lightweight when it came to confrontations, had hesitated before stepping into this lion's den to ask for special consideration.

'You want sob stories? I got plenty of

them. My two best people are out sick. My backlog is piled high here. You know we also do all the County cases and some other municipalities contract stuff out to us as well, right?

'Every week or two, I get this same desperate plea from one of you guys about just this one case, just this one time. I got the scars from all these 'just-this-one-timers,' Detective. Do you want to come over and see them? For the last time, you get in line and you wait your turn! Do I make myself clear?'

'Can you at least give me an idea of how long we are talking?'

'It takes what it takes. Maybe a week, maybe two. Maybe more.'

'I'll check back with you in a few days,' Frank said.

'Just remember, the more I'm on the phone with *you* guys, the longer it's going to take me to get my *real* work done!' Morgan barked. '*Are we done here?*'

'Yeah. We're done here.'

As bad as his conversation had gone with Morgan over expediting the ballistics reports, his earlier conversation with the medical examiner had been even worse. By comparison Morgan was a total sweetheart.

Ballistics, as Morgan unhesitatingly pointed out, honored contracts with multiple agencies, but the ME's regional responsibilities extended even further afield, and their plate was stacked even higher.

On top of that, the county coroner was an elected office, and this was a reelection year, which added exponentially to the agenda — and the stress factor.

Frank was hardly a shrinking violet but he had backed off from the fire-breathing individual on the other end of the phone, who had seemed ready to make it downright personal during that brief but memorable exchange.

He had encountered more equitable responses in his quest to expedite blood work and prints from the lab, but ultimately they had turned him down just as thoroughly, only in a nicer manner. Things were tough all over.

The bottom line was that none of the information he desperately needed would be forthcoming in the immediate future. He was on his own.

But when the technology wasn't forthcoming, Frank mused, maybe a dinosaur was exactly what was needed.

Frank, still at his desk back at the precinct, took another deep breath, and perused the list of names he had jotted down during his interview with Anita.

There was no question about it. Al Land was not the most popular man in town. There were many people who bore grudges toward Al of some sort.

Frank needed to work smart, pare the list down to the most plausible leads, and start with those. Maybe he'd get lucky. If that didn't work, he'd have to go back and work his way down the list thoroughly, one by one. He didn't relish that task.

He was lucky enough to catch Anita on the second ring and ask to meet so they could follow up on that first conversation.

They exchanged no false pleasantries but got right to it. It didn't surprise Frank that Anita was composed, without any outward sign of grief. It suited her character.

'Anita, tell me about some of the people you mentioned. Who strikes you as having it in for Al the most?'

'Well, he did have that run-in with Billy Wilde last year.'

Billy Wilde was no stranger to the authorities. Officially, he owned several garbage disposal companies with lucrative contracts with the local municipalities. Unofficially, he was well known to people like Frank for other reasons, including his gambling interests and a lovely variety of other illicit operations.

There were several racketeering indictments in process against him, and Frank's own department was currently investigating rumors of a homicide he might have had a hand in, with little to go on. Wilde spent much of his life in court. He employed at least a dozen attorneys and thus far seemed untouchable.

'Yeah, I remember when you told me that. What was the beef between them?'

'Billy suspected his wife was less than faithful, he's kinda paranoid that way, and he hired us to look into it. Al found absolutely nothing out of line with the wife, but then Billy came back and had us follow his girlfriend as well, thinking she was double-timing him too.'

'Hard to find a faithful spouse any more.' Frank smirked.

'Turns out Al couldn't find either of the gals doing a blessed thing wrong. His wife shopped and lunched with her friends. His girlfriend just shopped. But Billy wouldn't believe Al.

'One day in a bar, they had it out and Billy refused to pay Al the remainder of his fee until he came back with some results that he liked better.'

'Most guys would have been relieved to learn there actually was no, er, correspondent, in that kind of case,' Frank said. 'Go figure.'

'Yeah, well, Billy hates to be proven wrong about anything. It was a bit of a tense conversation. But I've been thinking about it and I can't see Billy doing something like this. He's nasty but more thoughtful, if you know what I mean.

'He and Al were still arguing about the payment, but it hadn't reached a stage past that posturing stuff. And Billy would've sent Al a warning first. At the very worst, if he had gone drastic on us, he would have done something cleaner.

'One day Al would just not have been here anymore, and nobody would've seen nothing. This was just plain sloppy.'

'I'll look into it anyway. Who else rises to the top?'

'Scudder — maybe.'

Frank checked his notes. 'Duane Scudder. As in Scudder Investigations?'

'The same. He and Al were on the force together briefly. Scudder cashed out on his retirement a few years after Al left, and opened his own agency. He and Al were known to step on one another's toes now and then in the pursuit of clients.'

'Hardly reason to shoot someone.'

'Not likely, I'll grant you. But Scudder's got a bad temper. Al tells me he hurt a few people when he was a cop but his connections in the department were always reputable enough to let him slide past it. But in private business it was a whole different story. He's messed up a few deals, and Al was always there to step in and scoop up the clients while they were still upset. The two of them were definitely not on speaking terms.'

'Could you actually see Scudder doing something this drastic, though?'

'Duane? Uh-uh. What I'm thinking though is, he's got a lot of young tough guys working for him, not the brightest bulbs in the box by any means, the kind who wouldn't be above looking to make a name with him if they heard him bad-mouthing someone, you know?'

'Like a young guy in a hoodie and a beat-up Blazer? Would he have that kind of guy working for him?'

She hesitated. 'Possibly. Just a thought.'

'Incidentally . . . what about that shooting that was in the paper last year involving Al?' Frank asked. 'Any possibility of a reprisal?'

'Ha! That? I seriously doubt it. Didn't even think it was worth mentioning. We helped out a skip-tracer find a guy who had jumped bail. The bondsman stood to lose a good hunk of money. The guy turned out to be armed with some pea shooter starter pistol; he took a blind shot, hit Al in the leg, then got all scared, dropped the gun and gave up without a fight. The guy was still apologizing when they got him back to lockup. He's been in prison ever since.'

'But maybe a relative or friend . . . '

'Doesn't feel right to me, but knock yourself out.'

Frank was jotting down additional thoughts in his notes when Anita added, 'But the one that would stand out to me is the DKM gang.'

Another name that needed no introduction to Frank. 'Do tell.'

'He made *lots* of enemies on that one. I wouldn't know where to begin. A lot of indignant little twerps jumped on the bandwagon when the word *harassment* first started coming up.'

'But I'm thinking, we're talking stuff like whistle-blowers and media crusader types, Anita. Not the kind to pull out a gun and shoot somebody.'

'De-*tec*-tive, my husband was killed by an amateur. You know that and I know that. The DKM thing is crawling with people out of their element, ticked off to the max, pushed to their limits, frustrated

65

and willing to believe that Al was Satan himself. I would *not* dismiss the possibility. You asked me.'

'Okay, okay.' Short pause. 'Anita, I also have to ask you this . . . '

'I bet I know what's coming. Was Al fooling around, was there a jealous husband or boyfriend or something? As the *cliché* goes, he was no choirboy, but no, there had not been anyone like that . . . in some time.'

'Uh . . . forgive me, but, you seem awfully sure of that, Anita. Couldn't there . . . '

'Detective, Al and I were straight with each other. That's one thing we were, was honest with one another. Believe me when I tell you this: he would have told me if something was going on. I would take that to the bank.'

Why did his conversations with this woman elicit such deep sighs from him?

'Okay, Anita. Anybody else or does that do it for now?'

'That's all I got. Go find the schmuck that did this.'

When Jilly returned to Marina Belize's condo later that evening, she wasn't sure what to expect, but hoped at least to encounter more people who could tell her something about the enigmatic Marina.

Something wasn't fitting.

According to her sister Jané, Marina loved to dance and was full of life. She had a boyfriend who looked to be a bad boy for sure. Yet according to Marina's co-workers and so far her neighbors, she was decidedly quiet and private. How to reconcile these two sides?

She was surprised to find the door to Marina's condo standing open when she came down the hall.

She peeked in. Two young men were dragging large cardboard cartons across the carpet. A woman was kneeling on the floor, filling another box with small articles. She turned around and looked up inquiringly as Jilly entered.

'Detective!'

'Hello, Jané. Packing up Marina's things?'

Jané looked somewhat guilty. The two men, who also looked Brazilian, moved to stand protectively beside her and stared at Jilly silently.

'I thought I might as well get started on it. There's nobody else to do this. I need something to keep me busy, you know?'

'I can understand that,' Jilly said, eyeing the two men. They weren't particularly threatening but they did look apprehensive. Jané quickly stood up.

'This is my husband, Eddie.' She gestured to the taller of the two, a lean guy in a shirt with a soccer team logo.

He nodded at Jilly.

'And this is his brother, Martin.' Jilly nodded back at both. They continued to stand and stare mutely at her.

'You know,' said Jilly evenly, 'there might be a clue in here that could help us find Marina's killer. I'm thinking you shouldn't be moving all this stuff out so quickly.'

Almost as if they wanted to clear it out before she could get to it, she thought to herself.

'Oh, I didn't think of that,' Jané

responded. 'Of course. But do you really think there could be any kind of clue in this stuff?'

'Jané, I have no idea, but I have to consider everything. And I'd think you'd want me to be doing that. Tell me really, why are you here doing this right now?'

The postures of the two young men turned subtly more aggressive, or so it seemed to Jilly. Instinctively she balanced her weight on both feet and moved her hand closer to her bag and the gun within, while remaining outwardly casual. Best to be ready for anything in this situation.

Eddie, never taking his eyes off Jilly, muttered something in Portuguese to Jané. She shook her head and made a gesture towards him as if to wave him off. Something seemed to defuse, although everyone was still clearly apprehensive. Jané turned back to Jilly:

'I'm not sure, but I think you're someone I can trust — a little bit,' she said.

'I'd like to think so. But it will depend on what you tell me. So I can make no promises, Jané. But I *am* the most trustworthy investigator you're going to get in this case, I will guarantee you that.'

Jané considered Jilly's statement for a moment and finally, with a sag of her shoulders, said, 'Let's sit down over there,' motioning to a sofa and chairs. 'It's a long story.'

★   ★   ★

The story began with the most formidable criminal element in Brazil's most celebrated city.

Comando Vermelho, or The Red Command, is one of the most powerful and feared cartels in Rio de Janeiro. It began as a dissident political group in the early 1980s but gradually shed its ideological base and degenerated into an out-and-out criminal organization, dealing in drug and arms trafficking.

At some point, a splinter faction broke off, seeking its own power and means, and began to engage in a particularly vicious battle with its parent organization (who dismissively called it the 'Little

Command') over control of certain neighborhoods in the city. Not only were members of both groups in constant peril for their lives in this merciless struggle, but so were their families and friends.

There was no such thing as a civilian in this war. Anyone could and would be made a brutal casualty — and an example — if the opportunity arose.

Paulinho Silva, one of the major leaders of the Little Command, made the decision to send his family out of the country some ten years earlier. His wife had not escaped — Red Command 'soldiers' had located her — but their two daughters reached the United States safely and changed their surnames to Belize.

Paulinho hoped that his enemies would never find them. The sisters never learned what fate had finally befallen their father, but for the past ten years they had lived quietly and without incident in this same city.

Jané met and married a loving, reliable, and hard-working Brazilian man, while Marina completed her education and found a good job at which she excelled.

They both tried to keep reasonably low profiles, lead quiet lives and not make waves, and they had come to believe they were secure in their new identities, safely off the radar of the vengeful criminals of Rio.

But they both loved to dance, and the one thing in which they indulged themselves was the occasional evening out at a local dance club.

And Marina's eye could not always overlook any handsome, flashily-dressed young man who offered to partner her.

Eventually she fell into a dubious but exciting love relationship. And, of course, when Marina was brutally murdered, that was precisely where Jané's thoughts went.

And the one person that might have been tempted to sell Marina out to her enemies was Ricky Wright.

★   ★   ★

When Jané finished, Jilly said, 'You think, then, that there's evidence here in Marina's place of who she really is

— who you both really are?'

Jané nodded, tears forming in her eyes.

'We weren't supposed to keep photos of Mama and Papa, letters, keepsakes, anything about them at all — but I think Marina might have. Who knows if the Comando has people here in this city, or even just 'friends'? If anything were to be found here, anything at all . . . '

Jilly nodded. The two men stared at her from their seats, still suspicious.

'You were right to tell me this,' Jilly finally said, gently. 'Perhaps this had nothing to do with the Comando. But if it did, I promise we can and will protect you.'

'I was convinced — we were both convinced — that Papa was dead and the war was over, that they were all dead and gone. And we were safe.'

'And maybe you are right, Jané. I'm going to look into this. But for the moment, I'm going to need you to leave all of Marina's things here.'

She took out her cell phone and keyed in a familiar number. 'I'm going to get a team over here to seal this off and keep an eye on the place. I'll also order a police guard for you while we figure this out. As soon as the officers are here to accompany you, you should all leave.'

Jilly further instructed them to continue to keep a low profile and watch out for each other, but to otherwise act normally — and let her know of any new developments — while she tried to ascertain if a danger actually existed from the horrific cartel six thousand miles away.

5

Al Land's most notorious recent client was Alfonse D'Yquem — elusive, seclusive, and not just rich but filthy rich. He was the brains and sheer power behind the digital mega-giant Prophet DKM.

At nineteen, he had founded the company along with two partners, computer wizards like himself, but both several years his senior. Within two years he had bought out one and outmaneuvered the other.

He was responsible for a number of brilliant technical innovations, and combined an aptitude and taste for cutthroat business practices. He grew his enterprise at impressive speed but always, somehow, out of the public eye.

Seemingly innumerable mergers and acquisitions all enhanced DKM as it evolved into a shadowy empire that spanned first the country, then the continent, and finally the globe, quietly dominating a considerable corner of the digital industry.

Al had worked on contract and retainer for D'Yquem and his companies for several years, partially because, being based in New Orleans, he was local to DKM's corporate headquarters and partly because of his reputation as a rough-edged, unprincipled crumb who was most comfortable operating in the shadows.

This was precisely the kind of guy, Frank mused, that a spectral and ruthless nabob like D'Yquem would find useful. At the time of his demise, Al was under multiple subpoenas stemming from allegations that he had attempted to intimidate not only plaintiffs and witnesses in a lawsuit against D'Yquem, but also several journalists reporting on the case.

It was a high-profile ongoing story that the media, stung by threats to their own, had been riding ceaselessly, to the great distaste of Al and his employer.

Frank figured it would be next to impossible to reach D'Yquem directly, and he was right. He did have a phone conversation with an unctuous, officious little irritant from company twelve, battalion six of the DKM legal department. He was told the earliest he could possibly speak with anyone was the next morning, and that he should ask for Jan DeVries in the security department.

A few more phone calls convinced Frank that Anita had been correct in giving a low priority to the bail-jumper who had taken a shot at Al. His name was — no kidding — Johnny Doe. He was currently serving a sentence in a state prison a hundred miles away and would be doing so for the foreseeable future.

As far as Frank could ascertain, Doe had no living family, no relatives, and no close friends locally. He was a transient from Arkansas who, newly arrived in town, had immediately gotten himself into stupid trouble.

Frank wasn't totally ready to write him off, but felt he could safely be shelved in favor of more promising leads. The next possibility to come to mind was Duane Scudder.

★ ★ ★

Scudder Investigations occupied most of the third floor of a building that had seen better days. Frank had debated the relative merits of calling ahead or showing up cold and had decided on the latter.

As luck would have it, the receptionist informed him that Mr. Scudder was indeed in his office, and if he wouldn't mind waiting, she'd check on his availability.

There was, remarkably, only a short wait before Duane Scudder blew through the door into the waiting room, a huge smile on his face, and extended his hand in greeting to Frank, who rose from the overstuffed sofa.

'Always delighted to help out law enforcement,' Scudder gushed in a deep voice.

Frank wondered if the guy consciously worked on resembling an actor playing a PI on a television show — flashy dress, styled hair, Pepsodent grin, and clearly diligent at maintaining a youthful look despite the onset of years.

'Come on into my office and tell me what I can do for you, Detective, uh . . . '

'Vandegraf. Frank Vandegraf.' He followed Scudder back through the door into a small but nicely-appointed office and sat himself down in front of a large, surprisingly empty desk. Scudder deposited himself behind it and waited expectantly.

'Al Land,' Frank began. Scudder nodded vigorously.

'A shame, a real shame. Just terrible.'

Crocodile tears. This was beginning to look fairly promising, Frank mused to himself. He kept his eyes on Scudder, looking for any tells.

'You knew him well?'

'Of course. We were on the force together for a while. After we had both gone private, we crossed paths quite often. It was inevitable. This isn't all that big a city.'

'Did you get along?'

Scudder shook his head and looked down at his desk, a half-grin twisting his mouth. 'Not really. No.'

Frank waited a few beats. Finally Scudder continued.

'Al was a pain in the neck, Detective. I

won't lie to you about that. He was a weasel. Unprincipled. A bottom feeder — let's just say he'd stoop to activities I wouldn't. He'd steal clients. Look for unethical advantages and shortcuts. He would undercut anyone he felt was his competition, and that was sometimes me.'

'So you didn't get along.'

Scudder met his gaze evenly. 'Of course not. And I think you knew that. Are you also thinking I had something to do with his murder?'

'Honestly? No. But maybe somebody you know might know something?'

Scudder leaned across the desk, his arms crossed, keeping his eyes locked on Frank. His words were measured. The Hollywood façade was gone.

'What exactly do you mean?'

'How many employees do you have, Mr. Scudder?'

'Scudder Investigations employs nine people. Our receptionist Janet, whom you met, two administrative assistants, a clerical intern, and five field operatives, who perform a large range of duties outside of the office. We also have an

80

accounting firm and an attorney on retainer. Not a huge operation, but we do cover a lot of ground.'

'You had some public disagreements with Al?'

'Yes, I did.'

'And how about your staff members? Did any of them ever cross paths with him?'

'Not that I know of. Would you care to ask any of them yourself?'

'In due time, yes. Let's you and I talk some more first.'

Scudder conspicuously checked his watch. 'I've got fifteen minutes before I need to be somewhere. Go ahead. But maybe I can save you some time. Al died on Thursday, correct?'

'That's right.'

'I happened to be out of town, traveling to three cities, for the past week, and just returned on the red eye this morning. It's an easy enough matter to show you plane tickets, hotel and restaurant credit receipts.'

'Well, that *is* convenient,' Frank said, allowing himself the slightest of smiles.

'I travel a lot. I give seminars on

81

security. You might enjoy one some time. Let me know and I'll comp you.'

Frank rubbed the back of his neck, reflecting that Scudder didn't feel right for this anyway, either to carry it out, or to consciously order it done. It was a rash and stupid act, and this was anything but a rash and stupid man.

His hired help on the other hand . . .

'Okay. Let's talk about your field operatives,' Frank said.

Two of Scudder's field agents were female — so much for Anita's 'a lot of young tough guys' — and the where-abouts of two others, including Scudder's second in command, could be verified for all of that Thursday night, since both had been on assignment. That left only Scudder's most recent hire, Gerald Lombard, whom he had taken on right out of community college. Lombard happened to be off that day.

Scudder, at Frank's urging, described him. 'Hard-working guy. He was happy to get a job. I gotta say, not the most intelligent employee in the office, but he makes up for it in enthusiasm. Eager to help out around here, puts in a lot of hours, never complains.'

He buzzed the receptionist to bring in Lombard's file. 'We naturally checked him out. Clean record, never any problems with the law, not even juvie stuff. I took him out in the field a few times and he did well. Handled himself well.'

'By that you mean he handled himself well in physical confrontations, that sort of thing?'

'I mean he couldn't be intimidated. He stood his ground. He wasn't the type that went looking for a fight, but he made it quite clear that he wasn't going to back down from one either.'

'Do you know of any physical fights involving him?'

'No, nothing ever came to that. And Gerry isn't pushy. He's actually a pretty easy-going guy.'

'Does he carry a weapon?'

'All my operatives are required to undergo training in the use of weapons — and to qualify for up-to-date carry permits, yes. Gerry is a decent shot, if a bit inexperienced, but I have to say he seems a bit reluctant with a sidearm.'

'Does he carry it when he's not working?'

'Most of the jobs here are pretty routine, chasing down information, and that sort of thing, and in those cases a few of our ops prefer to lock up their weapons in the office, especially when they're off work. He's almost always one of them. Ah . . . thanks, Janet.'

The receptionist had entered and placed a manila folder in front of him on the desk. He passed it over to Frank.

'I can't see Gerry being involved in this in any way,' Scudder said as Frank browsed the few brief pages and looked at Lombard's photo and vital statistics. He had dark hair. About the right height and weight.

'Just routine. This his current address, 9600 Dorritt?' Frank jotted down the information in his notebook.

'That would be it.'

'Would you happen to know what kind of car Mr. Lombard drives?'

'I'm not sure. I've seen him pull up in

the parking lot. Maybe a Jeep Cherokee or a Bronco or something like that. Light, maybe white or beige. Some kind of utility vehicle, which as you know are pretty common right now.'

Some investigator, thought Frank. He didn't seem to be all that observant when it came to his employees. 'Later model? Older?'

'Oh, it's a few years old. A little beat up.'

'Possibly a Blazer?'

Scudder shrugged. 'Certainly that type of vehicle.'

'So you are saying that Gerald's weapon is here on the premises? Can that be confirmed?'

'Certainly.' It was said somewhat grudgingly. Scudder picked up his phone and keyed in a few numbers, spoke briefly, replaced the receiver. 'This doesn't sound so routine anymore, Detective.'

Frank shrugged. 'Just covering all the possible bases, Mr. Scudder.'

Scudder's phone buzzed and he picked up, uttered a few more words and again hung up.

'Yes, Gerry's weapon is in the safe. You're not saying you need to see it?' The words sounded accommodating but Scudder's expression was anything but. Frank realized he would likely need a warrant to look at that gun. He shook his head.

'Not just yet. But I might be back.' He stood up from his chair. 'Thanks for your help.'

Scudder also rose and extended his hand to shake, but remained behind his desk. 'Any time. Always happy to help out the police.' The Pepsodent grin was gone.

'No need to walk with me, I can find my way out,' Frank smiled wryly and turned to the door.

★ ★ ★

It was a short drive to Western Waste Removal, Billy Wilde's flagship company. Frank decided he'd take a chance on a cold call and Billy actually being there, just to see if his luck continued to hold out.

Wilde was infamous for his extremely low profile and this facility, in line with that reputation, consisted of a small low building and a lot filled with garbage trucks.

The garbage itself was carted off site to a dumping area, but the place still did not exactly smell like a garden. Drivers and others in blue jumpsuits bustled everywhere. Wilde was indeed in his office, and when notified by his secretary told her to let Frank in.

His executive office looked more like a large storage room with desks, tables and chairs piled high with papers and folders, and a line of jammed old file cabinets along one wall.

'I think I know you,' Wilde said in a hoarse voice. He was heavyset, impatient, with a definite underlying air of menace — not a man to mess with. He made no effort to shake Frank's hand but directed him to a chair.

'Possibly,' Frank replied, shifting a pile of forms to another chair and sitting. 'I certainly know you.'

'Cop, yes?'

'Detective. Frank Vandegraf.'

'So what do you want?' Wilde asked.

Again, right to the point, which was fine with Frank. 'You knew Al Land.'

'Ah. Yeah, sure I did. I figured that might be it, why you're here. I heard about him the other night.'

'Seems like everybody did. Tell me about you and him.'

Wilde shrugged, casually shuffled some of his own papers around on his desk as he spoke. 'Not much to tell. He did some work for me. We weren't like friends or anything. Don't know much about the guy, to tell the truth. Taciturn sort.'

'I hear you had an argument a while back?'

'Who told you that? That wife of his? Aargh. Now she's a piece of work, that one. I wouldn't exactly call it an argument, uh . . . what's your name again?'

'Detective Vandegraf.' This guy was not going to call him Frank, not by any stretch.

'Okay, Detective. I'm sure I know you! I do, don't I? This was more like a disagreement. A misunderstanding over services rendered and fees. We were

88

working it out, he and I. We're business-men. We understood how to deal with misunderstandings, if you get me?'

'He didn't get you the results you wanted?' Frank asked.

'I at first thought he hadn't been sufficiently thorough. Turns out I may well have been wrong, but for a long time we were discussing that issue. Nothing more.'

'Just covering all the bases,' Frank replied, pulling out his notebook while still keeping an eye on Wilde's facial expressions. 'Let's talk a little about that, and about your whereabouts Thursday night, if you don't mind.'

'You don't seriously think I had anything to do with Al's death?' Wilde asked, clearly surprised — to Frank it seemed genuine.

He began to laugh, shook his head as if in disbelief. 'Oh no, this is a joke! You said you know me, right?'

Frank just stared. Wilde stared back.

After a long silence, he said, 'If you think I did this then maybe you don't know me. Not like you think you do, okay? That's all I have to say. Now if you'll forgive me, I got work to do, a company — a few companies — to run.'

He looked down and began to sort through the forms before him. The interview was done.

Frank stood up and pocketed his notebook. He had gotten what he needed here. 'I might be back for more questions.'

'If you do come back,' muttered Wilde without looking up, 'be prepared to bring me in. With my lawyer. We're done here.'

Returning to his car, dodging garbage trucks in the lot, Frank reflected, *Maybe Wilde ordered the hit. I can't dismiss it out of hand. But something just doesn't feel right about it. Something hasn't felt right about anything today.*

He did, however, suddenly have the urge, when he had a moment, to look into the current health and whereabouts of Wilde's wife . . . and girlfriend. Just out of curiosity.

★ ★ ★

Frank's last stop of the day, he fervently hoped, as he observed darkness beginning to fall, was to 9600 Dorritt — Gerald Lombard's address, a two-story apartment house that looked to house perhaps eight units, with access to the upper apartments via scattered stairways to an outer balcony that ringed the building.

There was a fenced pool to the rear with the metal gate ajar. He found the name on the row of buttons and rang. A voice came through the fuzzy intercom.

'Yeah, who is it?'

'Police,' Frank spoke into the grille. 'Detective Vandegraf. Can I have a few words?'

There was no answer. A moment later the intercom clicked off.

He heard a door open on the second floor, towards the rear, on the balcony. Steps running.

Lombard was moving!

Frank wheeled around, looking for access to the rear. He heard footsteps going down concrete stairs to the outdoor pool area.

Oh no. He hated this.

He surprised himself with his relative quickness as he took off, hitting the metal gate to the pool area and pushing it open with a smash. Lombard was on the next to last step of the staircase from the second floor, glancing over his shoulder at him.

Frank made a quick calculation. He could still intercept him as he went around the deserted pool and the chairs.

They met at a corner of the pool, with only a few moments to spare before the younger man would be able to outdistance him. Frank gasped an epithet and shoved him in.

★ ★ ★

'Would you like to explain to me why you took off like that?' Frank asked him a few minutes later.

Lombard, soaking wet, was sitting on a deck chair, his arms cuffed behind him, looking alternately defiant and miserable.

A number of tenants had come out to investigate the commotion and Frank periodically flashed his badge and ordered them to go back inside.

No doubt many of them were curiously peering through the blinds of their windows at them now.

'How'd you find me?' was the only reply Lombard would give.

Frank looked him over, tried to imagine him in a dark hoodie. It would work.

'Went to the source. Your boss.'

Genuine shock. 'Duane? What does he know about this?'

'So you're saying you were alone in this, right?'

'What? Wait. What are you talking about? Alone in *what*?'

'Suppose you tell me, Gerald? What did you do that made you panic and run when a cop came to your door? Don't you work with cops and law enforcement types all the time?'

'I was only trying to help. I didn't mean any harm. Nobody got hurt.'

Frank stopped at that. 'What do you mean, nobody got hurt? You *killed* him, for Pete's sake!'

Lombard froze and stared at Frank, not comprehending.

'What — what are you talking about? Nobody got killed!'

Frank wondered how often in the course of the day he unconsciously rubbed the back of his neck, like he caught himself doing right now. 'What are *you* talking about?'

'Amanda! I was just trying to help Amanda out of a jam!'

'Who's Amanda?'

'Amanda Darcy. She works with me at Duane's agency, she's the intern there. Isn't that why you're here?'

'Uhhh . . . no. No, Amanda is not why I am here, Gerald. Let's take you upstairs and inside and dry you off and we'll talk about this. But the cuffs stay on until I decide if I like your story.'

'If it's all the same with you, can we stay out here?'

Lombard looked downright alarmed at the prospect of returning to his apartment.

'So . . . there's something, maybe some kind of contraband, up in your place, is that what I'm hearing? Something Amanda wanted you to hold on to for her?'

'Ohhh man,' Lombard moaned, mostly to himself. 'I am so screwed. My job is *gone*! Am I gonna get time for this? We thought it'd all be okay. I was just trying to help . . . '

Frank couldn't wait to see what it was. Drugs, he figured. Narcotics. Cocaine. Guns? How did this fit in with the shooting of Al Land, and what was he involved in? This might be bigger than he had possibly imagined! How big a headache was this going to turn out to be?

*   *   *

When it was all sorted out, Frank felt badly, but he had little choice but to call for uniformed backup to come pick up Lombard and confiscate the contents of the apartment.

'Now let me get this straight,' he said to Lombard as they waited for the uniforms to arrive.

He gestured all around, at the endless stacks of cardboard boxes that jammed the living room to a height of maybe

95

seven feet, with only narrow corridors left between them. 'Cigarettes? Really?'

Lombard, sitting on the arm of a ratty chair, still cuffed, hung his head and was barely audible. 'Her cousin Randy brought them in from across the state line. The taxes are less there, and he can sell them cheap and make a fortune.'

'I hate to tell you this, Gerald, but there are *no* tax stamps on these. These are stolen. His profit is better than you think. So he was going to cut you in on this?'

'It was just a favor,' Lombard murmured. 'For Amanda. She said she couldn't keep them anywhere in her place, and they had no other place for them. It was only for a few days . . . '

'Amanda must be pretty cute, I'd guess?'

'She's beautiful, actually.'

'And you and she . . . ?' Frank waved his finger back and forth, here and there.

Lombard nodded.

'Anybody else at work know about this?'

He shook his head. 'We kept it all a secret, our being together. And the cigarettes, of course. She couldn't trust anybody, but she said she could trust me.'

'And — just a wild guess — just before these cigarettes were coming into the picture, that was when she decided she wanted to be your girlfriend, right?'

'I know it sounds bad, but it's real.'

'Was she worth risking your whole future for, son?'

Lombard could only sadly nod. 'And we'll still be together when this is all done. We'll start a new life somewhere . . . '

Well . . . Scudder had said that Gerald was not his brightest employee, after all. Understatement indeed. This was a dim bulb if there ever was one. 'So when did these cigarettes start arriving here?'

'They dropped them off late Thursday, after dark. I helped unload them. We brought them in from the back alley. Took us hours, 'til past midnight.'

Frank felt with some certainty that, when Amanda Darcy and her 'cousin' got picked up, they'd corroborate that story, knowingly or otherwise. Or if by some fluke of luck they had already made their successful getaway, there would be a paper trail for a rented truck or something else that bore out his story about Thursday night. He just knew it.

Gerald Lombard was a fool, and he was about to become not only unemployed but likely incarcerated. But he was not a killer. At least he was not the killer that Frank was looking for.

Hang the luck.

Frank turned back to Lombard.

'Another question, Gerald. What kind of vehicle do you drive?'

'A Cherokee, ten years old. Pale green, out front. Why?'

'Just wondering. One last question. Did you ever hear your boss talk about a guy named Al Land?'

Gerald looked up, taken aback momentarily. 'Uh . . . sure. Duane always talks about him. He hates the guy, man. Why?'

'That's what I was afraid of,' Frank said, to nobody in particular. The intercom buzzed and he went to answer it.

6

Frank started the new day with a call back to DKM, asking to be put through to Jan DeVries, who turned out to be Assistant to the Head of Security and was, surprisingly, reasonably cooperative.

'We're sorry to hear of Mr. Land's death,' DeVries began smoothly. 'What can I do to help you?'

'Tell me about Land's services for you, what he was involved in.'

'There were allegations publicly made about irregularities in the company's business practices. The allegations were totally groundless and violated the non-disclosure agreements signed by several of our personnel and independent contractors.'

'Whistle-blowers, in other words,' Frank interjected.

'Well, there were those who used that expression, but in fact they were agitators, pure and simple. As I said, their accusations were groundless.'

'How did Al Land figure into this?'

'With accusations and counter-accusations flying, the media involved, lawsuits initiated, that type of thing, matters threatened to become unmanageable. It was all very irresponsible. We suspected some kind of industrial espionage, personnel plants in DKM to derail ongoing projects, concerns along those lines. Mr. Land had performed various functions on our behalf for some time. We were familiar with him, approved of his approach, and knew he was utterly reliable.

'We asked him to step in and investigate the backgrounds of the complainants, make confidential inquiries, and similar undertakings.'

'Some would say he was brought in for intimidation of the whistle-blowers.'

DeVries made a puffing sound in dismissal. 'Nobody was being intimidated. Mr. Land was investigating the covert associations of the troublemakers. We are a preeminent multinational company, Detective. We deal in sensitive, confidential leading-edge digital development. You can certainly understand that there are lots of unprincipled factions out there that would profit from harm to us. There are also people who claim our proprietary entities should be theirs.

'A company like DKM has to defend itself constantly. But first and foremost, we're also a responsible corporation. We do not involve ourselves in the kinds of unethical and frankly unwise practices that we were being accused of. It was all totally without merit and potentially toxic.'

'Toxic. Interesting word. Just what was the nature of the lawsuits that these individuals were bringing against the company?'

'They ranged over a large spectrum. Total shotgun approach. Alleged business practices such as extortion and espionage. Human resource issues such as abusive treatment, bullying, sexism, unjust termination. The contractors alleged theft of intellectual property. I can go on and on. You'd have to speak with our legal department but I believe at last count there were something like sixteen separate ongoing cases at various stages.'

'Who did Land report to at DKM?

Who gave him his orders?'

'I was his usual liaison. I acted as interface with our legal department, Human Resources, and others.'

'I assume his business with the company generally went smoothly? No notable differences of opinion or rough spots?'

'Mr. Land was a consummate professional. He understood our concerns and was familiar with the landscape. We were all on the same page. That's why we consistently employed his services.'

'Who were the people he personally dealt with — the 'troublemakers' as you call them?'

'There were perhaps a dozen individuals he was doing background checks on. Perhaps another dozen collateral individuals related to the issues. And, of course, the baseless harassment suits.'

'I'm going to need a list of all the people he had contact with, especially the ones bringing suit against him. Just curious, are any of them still with the company?'

'None of them are active. We severed any freelance contractor agreements with involved parties. Some of the employees brought legal injunctions against us and couldn't be terminated, so they are on administrative leave pending the outcomes. I'll have my assistant email you a list of everyone Mr. Land was 'backgrounding.''

Backgrounding. Frank shook his head. Corporate speak. 'Offhand, does anyone in particular strike you as having had it in for Al Land?'

'Hard to say. There were a few ringleaders beginning to emerge in the media flurry. Cassandra Washington comes to mind: she was perhaps the highest profile. Lester Lanier. Those two made the most outrageous allegations in the press about Mr. Land's supposed threats.'

Frank had a few more questions and asked if the list could be faxed to the department rather than emailed. That provoked a slight sniff from DeVries but he said they could indeed do that.

A few more calls established that Lester Lanier had been missing from town for over two weeks. A relative simply said that he was on an extended vacation somewhere in the Caribbean. The definite, if unspoken, impression given was that Lester was frightened of something or someone.

Cassandra Washington, on the other hand, was easy to reach. Frank arranged a meeting — but not at her home, she insisted. It would have to be on what she termed 'neutral ground.' She, too, seemed scared of the tentacles of DKM.

This might be the cutting-edge tech industry, Frank considered, but at least some of their techniques were still familiar to a Neanderthal like himself.

Hanging up, Frank wondered if this line of inquiry was going to be worth his time. Given the options of fight or flight, all these people, when threatened, seemed to be more inclined to flight. Still he had to be thorough, despite the insane morass of enmities surrounding Al Land.

But he increasingly liked the other theory stirring in the back of his brain, the one that was gradually being reinforced by tidbits he turned up.

Frank stared at his car keys on the desk next to his phone. It was time to get back out on the street. But first he took a moment to flip through his ever-growing notes. He had gotten thoroughly caught up in them when his phone rang. 'This is Mallory, down at the desk. There's someone here to see you. I'm sending her up, okay?'

Now what?

A woman of perhaps fifty, jaw firmly set, came up the stairs to the squad room and looked around. The various personnel milling around paid her scant attention. She called out in a loud and hoarse voice, 'Where's Vandegraf?'

'That would be me, ma'am,' Frank called out, walking over to greet her. 'How can I help you?'

He seated her at his desk and quickly learned she was Mrs. Catherine Foster, the widowed mother of Severin 'Sonny' Foster, one of the victims found at the Ready Rite parking lot. When Frank made the mistake of referring to him as Sonny she snapped at him: 'His name is Severin. That other name is something that street trash called him. So what are you doing to find the person who killed my Severin?'

'We're doing all we can, Mrs. Foster,' Frank replied, as patient as he could will himself to be.

'I'd like to believe that. But I have my doubts, Detective. Young kid, you probably have him pegged as a street hoodlum, from a bad neighborhood, am I right? You probably think that's all any of them are, don't you? Why do I think nothing is ever going to be done?'

'We treat every case equally, ma'am,' Frank said carefully.

'So why haven't you found somebody yet, can you tell me that?'

'Ma'am, you are probably not aware of this, but we had eight homicides that night. Eight. I am personally investigating four of them. You have to understand, we're stretched a little thin right now. I'm doing everything I can . . . '

'Like what?' she interrupted, anger growing in her voice. She was starting to tremble, her voice shaking with emotion. 'I'm just betting whoever those other victims are, they're people you put a higher value on than my boy! Why, it wouldn't surprise me if their killers are found *long* before anybody finds out who killed my Severin! That is, if you ever *do* find who did it!'

'I understand your concerns, Mrs. Foster. And I am very sorry for your loss. Believe me, that is not how we work around here. Everybody counts. Everybody.'

'I've had to raise that boy all by myself ever since his father passed away six years ago. Do you know what it's like to raise a teenager as a single mother? To be breadwinner and a parent? It's like being both father and mother! I've done what I could!' Frank saw a tear begin to form in the lady's eye.

'No, truthfully, I do not know what it is like, ma'am,' he said. He didn't know what else he could say. 'But I will find the person who took him away from you.'

She looked at him intensely for a long time. 'Promise me,' she said in almost a growl.

'Yes, I promise you.'

'We'll see about that,' she said more quietly. There were still a few tears and she wiped them away with the back of her hand. Frank looked around for tissues. There was a small box on a nearby desk that he grabbed and placed in front of her.

'Let me ask you some questions while you're here, about your son's friends, the people he associates with, that type of thing. Can we do that?' She nodded.

It was a good half hour later that he escorted her downstairs and once again promised he would find the murderer of Severin Foster.

The trouble was, of course, he knew he couldn't be sure he could keep that promise. But he felt he had to make it.

To be honest, he did feel a bit guilty. He had intended, without realizing it, to put the teenager's death on the back burner. Certainly the sheer complexity of Al Land's case had been distracting him, he had to admit.

There was something about the case of Nicholas Lowell that was compelling as well. But there were four cases here and, yes, they all counted. That had not just been something he had said to get Mrs. Foster off his back. Sonny Foster — and

Rudy Caliente — required his attention as well.

Another trip to his desk for his car keys. Another few minutes to refresh his memory on his recent notes. And then quickly, while he still could, he was out the door and off to his car.

★   ★   ★

3426 Hatchings was a two-story apartment building on a quiet street about a block off a major thoroughfare. Frank was not surprised when he rang the bell under the name 'Caliente/Carlisle' and got no answer. He got an immediate reply over the intercom when he buzzed the super.

'Yeah, who is it?' blared a woman's voice.

'Police. Detective Vandegraf.'

'You got more questions, huh?' the voice replied. 'Okay.' There was a buzz and Frank opened the barred door. Immediately down the hall, beyond the stairway, a door opened. A heavyset woman in an old sweatshirt and jeans stepped out, cigarette dangling from her mouth.

'Oh, a new guy. You here about Miz Carlisle too, I assume?'

Frank was momentarily taken aback. 'Somebody's been here about her?'

Now the woman looked surprised.

'Uh . . . *Yeah*-uh.' She said it with sarcasm as if the answer were obvious to anyone but a fool. 'Young guy. Mighta been Chinese?'

'Was his name Lee by any chance?' Frank asked, rubbing the back of his neck.

'That would be the one.'

Frank muttered something, hopefully inaudible, under his breath. She didn't seem to hear it and continued. 'How awful what happened to her. She was a very nice young lady.' She gave a world-weary shake of the head and a far-off look and took another puff from her butt before returning her gaze to Frank.

Frank was feeling a bit foolish all of a sudden. 'Uh, what happened to *her*. You mean . . . '

'The murder, I mean. That's why you guys are here.'

Tia Carlisle was dead also? One of the

other murders from the other night?

The woman gave Frank a skeptical look, raised an eyebrow. 'So, now, you must be looking for her husband, right?'

'Rudy Caliente, you mean. That's her husband?'

'I guess so. I mean, I don't ask questions. None of my business. They've lived here for a couple of years now. Anyway, he wasn't here when the other detective came by and he hasn't returned yet.' She peered at him expectantly.

'And I'm afraid,' Frank said, 'Mr. Caliente will not be coming back at all. May I come in and talk to you?'

★   ★   ★

Tooey's, though a small hole-in-the-wall lounge, was, quite possibly, single-handedly responsible for the local importation of most of South Africa's chromium.

Every surface in the place gleamed with a silvery mirror chrome finish. Jilly decided to leave her sunglasses on. Dan, who had gallantly offered to join her on this particular leg of the investigation, seemed extremely distracted, though it was most likely not from the chrome.

Despite it being fairly early in the day, there were three or four tight-muscled, pneumatic young women gyrating on an elevated catwalk to excruciatingly loud music, including one with long, thick bright red hair and a skimpy red outfit.

Probably Luisa, guessed Jilly, not quite sure why, other than the red hair, she had come to that conclusion. This type of place depressed her immensely.

Five guys of varying ages sat around the chrome bar that abutted the dancers' area, looking alternately jaded and desperate. The bartender confirmed Jilly's suspicions and called Luisa over after the song ended.

She sauntered up, taking a few moments to work one or two of the customers with a smile and a pat on the back.

'You wanta know about Ricky? He's not in any kind of trouble, is he?' Luisa had huge, deer-like brown eyes and glossy, suspiciously over-full lips that never seemed to be able to completely close. 'He's such a sweet guy, but the record business can be pretty nasty, can't it?'

'Record business?' Jilly asked.

'Yeah. Ricky works for Casablanca Records. He's helping me get a record deal. He's such a nice, generous guy.' She nodded excitedly.

Jilly looked over at Dan, who was looking back at her, and then down at her hands. 'Luisa, Ricky wasn't in the record business.'

When she looked up, Luisa was blankly staring at her, not reacting. The look was not so much deer-like now, as deer-in-the-headlights. Stuffed deer would be closer to the truth, Jilly decided. 'And I'm afraid something has happened to him.'

She waited for dawn to break in the ingenuous sky of the dancer's face.

The conversation went quickly and without much promise. Luisa seemed to know less about her supposed boyfriend/benefactor than Dan and Jilly did. As they were leaving, Jilly muttered to Dan, 'Geez, gives the rest of us redheads a bad name.'

'Intellectually, maybe,' mused Dan, looking back wistfully. He grinned at Jilly mischievously.

'Does she strike you as a cold-blooded killer?'

Dan shook his head. 'It'd take her an hour to figure out which end of the gun to point.'

'By the way, nice of you to volunteer to join up with me on this one, partner. Where next? Shall we split up again?'

Dan smiled at the jibe, even seemed to blush a bit. 'It was my pleasure to help out, partner. Yeah, I've got to follow up on Tia Carlisle. Catch up with you later, Jilly.'

★　★　★

After some time and effort, Frank tracked down Officer Pardo on car patrol and asked if she had a few minutes.

For the moment she was working without a partner because of how thinly the force had been stretched. She had had a busy morning but had been presented with a welcome lull for a lunch opportunity, so they sat at a fast food stand and talked over greasy cheeseburgers and fries.

'Sonny Foster,' Frank began. 'I spoke

with his mother today. She mentioned that he hung out with a few neighborhood kids. She didn't know any names.'

'Yes sir, there are a few who hang out there. Mostly teenagers, almost all boys, after school, weekends. The store tries to discourage them but if they purchase something now and then and don't bother the other customers or interfere with parking or the flow, the manager doesn't complain much.

'He doesn't let them change their oil or work on their cars in the lot but he does let them hang around and talk cars and sports, and so forth. You've seen the store. It's the kind of place where the store personnel don't want to be involved any more than they have to.'

'You can drop the 'sir,' Officer, feel free to call me Frank. Anybody stand out? Problem kids? Any fights, arguments . . . that type of thing?'

She relaxed a little, and he noticed her speech grew a bit less formal.

'Not really. A truancy now and then during school time. We've had to disperse them once or twice when they got a little rowdy. Once in a while there's an argument that gets loud. I've broken up a fight or two. Fist fights, old school. Minor stuff. There's never been any major incidents, no arrests, nobody giving us a hard time.

'No incidents with weapons or drugs or anything like that whatsoever. I couldn't even tell you any names, to be honest. Nobody seems to be gang-affiliated. They're basically good kids, I'd say. Gearheads, not punks or bangers.

'There's some peeling out in the lot, laying rubber. They do get out of hand like teenagers do. Now and then there's the typical young male posturing and arguing, and as I said, now and then a fight. It's all inconsequential.'

'So it's not like somebody was out for Sonny, no notable grudges?'

Pardo shook her head. 'Nothing stands out, nothing at all. I'll keep my eyes and ears open and let you know if anything comes up.'

'Anybody ever get ticketed? For moving violations, parking, stuff like that?'

'Yeah, likely. Not by me. I can ask the other units if you'd like.'

'Can't hurt, thanks. Especially that green car. Let me know if anybody ticketed a green car of any kind. That would be very helpful. Now, how about the other deaths? Know anything about any of them?'

'I never saw any of the others before. None of the regular patrol officers seem to have either. I don't think any of them frequented the Ready Rite.'

'Thanks, much appreciated. I'm going over to talk to the Ready Rite manager next. Anything you might come up with could be of help here.'

'I'll do what I can, sir.'

'And I told you,' Frank said, balling up the wrapper from his consumed burger as he stood up, 'cut that 'sir' stuff, okay, Pardo?'

★   ★   ★

'Yeah, I was the manager that night. I already told you guys everything I knew when it all happened.' His name was Sammy and he was maybe thirty, heavyset with dark hair, on the nervous side, eyes constantly shifting.

They stood awkwardly on either side of the cluttered counter. Frank flipped through his notebook for a moment before continuing.

'I understand. Bear with me here, if you would. Did you know any of the individuals who were killed that evening?' he asked.

'I'd seen the kid a few times. He hung around outside with his friends. Never spoke with him, didn't know his name or anything.'

'What can you tell me about the kids he hung out with?'

'Oh man, nothing, really. I've been manager here about five months now? The guy I replaced pulled me aside when I came on and gave me some advice.

'Part of it was not to confront any of the teenagers out front. He said to call the cops if customers complained or something really radical was going down, you know? Otherwise, he said, I was better off just leaving it alone. Mind my own business.'

'So you don't know anybody's name, or anything about any of them?'

'Zero,' Sammy said with a blank stare. 'Already told you guys all this. Like everyone else, I heard the noises. It was all confused, just a bunch of bangs and stuff, people running out to see what had happened. Didn't learn anything 'til the cops came in and started asking questions. None of the names meant anything to me.'

'And curiously,' Frank interjected, 'absolutely nobody else was outside either. Everyone was in the store and saw and heard nothing. That's pretty remarkable, don't you think, Sammy?'

Sammy just shrugged.

'Do you happen to recall anyone who you saw run outside when the action started?'

Sammy extended his lower lip as if he were actually engaged in thought but quickly shook his head.

Another heavy, resigned sigh. Frank wondered if he should patent his sigh. 'So nobody knew this kid, Sonny Foster, and nobody knew any of the people he associated with, even though they were out here, like, four or five nights a week, driving their cars around, coming in the store to buy stuff?'

'Well, yeah, they did come in to buy stuff,' Sammy said.

'But you don't remember anything about them. Any of them. Never talked with them, shot the breeze with them.'

'Shot the breeze?' Sammy asked, eyes blank. 'What's that mean?'

'Like, talked with them.'

'Maybe. Don't remember.'

Another thought occurred to Frank. 'Any of them ever try to buy beer? Or cigarettes?'

'Yeah, probably.'

'And you'd have to proof them, right? Look at their ID?'

'Oh yeah. That's a biggie around here. You get fired if you don't proof someone for that, or if you actually sell to them.'

'So . . . maybe someone had an ID, maybe a fake one?'

'Hey, I never sold anything to anyone with a fake ID. Or without ID. No way.' Now there was alarm in those previously blank eyes.

'No, that's not what I'm getting at, Sammy. I'm wondering if maybe you saw an ID with a name you might remember?'

The light went out again behind the eyes. There was a long pause before Sammy replied, 'Uh ... naw, I don't remember.'

Frank sighed. It had been worth a try.

The interview terminated shortly thereafter. Frank departed the Ready Rite knowing no more than he had when he came in. In fact, he thought to himself, was it possible he might now know even less? Guys like Sammy just had that effect.

7

Frank tried to put together the bizarre pieces shaping up in this insane jigsaw puzzle as he drove. Nick Lowell's phone had indeed shown a call, somewhat earlier that ill-fated day, to a restaurant called Langostino. A phone call confirmed that Lowell had made a reservation for two there that night.

He was headed there right now, and he had mixed feelings about where he was going. It was in his least favorite part of the city . . . the waterfront . . . and just a block around the corner from Saint Expedito, the bar where Al Land was killed.

Langostino was nicely furnished, casual but definitely upscale, with lots of faux-weathered wood paneling, and heavy oaken tables and chairs. Vintage tinted photos of scenes from long-ago harbors and fisheries were hung on the walls, which lent a sort of Steinbeckian air to the place, or so Frank thought, recalling photos he had seen in a book about the author once. It was low-lit and quiet. No doubt it would be quite crowded later in the evening.

The manager remembered Nick Lowell and his date from both a photo and the name. 'Certainly, Mr. Lowell has come here many times. I took his reservation myself. We reserved a special table for him and his guest. He requested our dessert chef prepare a special little chocolate raspberry torte for her — it was her birthday.'

'Did he ever bring other guests here?'

'Mr. Lowell had different companions, yes. He seems to enjoy the bachelor life. Is there a problem, Detective?'

'You might say that. I don't think Mr. Lowell will be enjoying much of any kind of life from here on out. He died late Thursday night.'

'My God, no!'

'I'm afraid so. So I do need to find out some information from you.'

'Why . . . why of course,' the manager sputtered. He was a neat little man with careful manners. 'May I ask what happened to him?'

'That, I am afraid, is what I am trying

to figure out. I know he came here and brought a young lady. What I *need* to know is what happened to them after they left.'

'We all know Mr. Lowell fairly well here. I think he wanted to impress the young lady so we made a little fuss over her. She seemed to like that.'

'Did she enjoy 'Happy Birthday' being sung to her by the wait staff?'

The little man sniffed distastefully. 'We don't quite do it that way, Detective. The waiter brought her the torte and I quietly came to the table to extend our best wishes. This isn't a diner.'

'So tell me about her. What did she look like?'

'She was a young Asian woman with dark hair, about shoulder-length. Very attractive. A particularly nice smile as I recall. She was wearing a simple but elegant ivory blouse and a mid-length taupe skirt, if memory serves me — minimal jewelry.'

Memory seemed to be serving — Frank had to admit — quite a course.

'Anything else you remember about the evening?'

'He gave her a present while they were having coffee and cordials. A bracelet, it looked like.'

'So when they left — did they seem cordial after the cordials?'

The manager allowed a small smile to crease the corners of his mouth. 'I try not to intrude upon the privacy of the guests, but, yes, they seemed quite happy and friendly with one another.'

'I assume you have valet parking?'

'Around here? We have to. Parking is at a premium, as you must have noticed. This is an old part of town. We have a parking lot but it's tiny.'

'Any idea who might have parked Lowell's car?'

'Actually, it was probably either Wayne or Sean. They're both on duty now.'

★   ★   ★

Sean, a lean young man whose hair and service jacket were both dark and very short, was trotting back to the valet stand as Frank approached. He remembered Lowell immediately from the photo and the description of the car.

'Of course I remember him. Man, he's a great tipper. We all keep our eyes peeled for that one. Flash guy, pretty cool. Usually has a nice lady with him too.'

'So you parked his maroon SUV last night?'

'Oh yeah. It was a busy night. I had to take it about a block and a half away to find a parking spot. But that's why you pay us. We know how to find the good spots, where the car won't be touched up and you don't have to walk.'

'Tell me exactly where you parked it, if you can remember? Was it anywhere near Saint Expedito?'

Sean smiled. 'Yeah! In fact I parked it just about in front of Saint Expedito! How'd you know that?'

Frank rubbed the back of his neck. 'Let's just say I'm psychic.'

'Uh . . . this got anything to do with the stuff that went down at Saint Expedito that night?'

Frank stared at the young man briefly. 'And what stuff would that be?'

'The crazy witch with the gun.'

Frank momentarily buried his face in his hand. 'Maybe you better tell me exactly what you mean.'

'I'm running over to get Mr. Lowell's car. I'm about maybe twenty feet away, and I see it's boxed in by some jerk's beat-up old SUV, and I'm trying to figure out what I'm gonna do when the guy tears out of the bar, jumps in the beater and peels out. He musta had the engine going.

'A few seconds later this lady comes running out, stands stock in the middle of the street, takes this stance like cops on TV' — he assumed a two-hand, locked-elbow, spread-legged pose — 'and pumps a round at the guy from about a half-block away. Then she runs up to this car parked right in front of Mr. Lowell's. She backs right into Mr. Lowell's car and leaves a dent in his fender, then peels out after the guy. I had to go explain that one to Mr. Lowell and he wasn't too happy. But he was cool, said it wasn't my fault.'

So much for using the valet to keep your car from being touched up, Frank thought. 'She took a shot at him. You're sure?'

'Oh yeah, for sure. No mistake there.'

'What can you tell me about this, uh, crazy witch with the gun?'

'I don't know. Dark clothing. Jacket came down below her waist. Looked like she might be blonde but I'm not sure.'

'See her car?'

'Yeah, it was a silver Lexus.'

'And that you're sure of?'

'Oh yeah . . . I notice cars like that.'

'So she took off down the street after the guy in the truck. Notice anything about the SUV?'

'Dirty white beat-up piece of junk, might have been a Blazer.'

'Anything else you remember at all?'

Sean gave that a moment. 'I'm afraid not, Detective.'

'Here's my card. If you think of anything else at all, it would be a great help if you called me.'

The valet took the card and pocketed it. 'Is Mr. Lowell all right?'

Frank looked at the earnest young man and put his hand on his shoulder. 'Not exactly, I'm afraid.'

'Jilly, you know I'd help you out if I could, but we're jammed. I can't move anything up.'

After several unsuccessful conversations going up the ladder at the crime lab, Jilly had finally arrived at the very top. Lauren Ochoa, who oversaw the entire operation, had a friendly history with her going back to their earliest days in the department and might have even owed her a favor or two, but this time she was stymied.

At least Lauren was being cordial despite the obvious strain and weariness in her voice. 'Look, you know about the big blow-ups with the brass. We're still recovering from that. It's all just really bad timing. If this had been before that . . . '

Jilly nodded behind her phone, leaning back in her chair. She had gotten wind of the major to-do of the previous week involving the higher-ups. It was a perfect storm of short-staffing, backlogs and political pressures. The worst possible time to come up with four more major crimes — eight, she corrected herself, remembering Frank's cases. She caught herself in her mental drift.

'Check back with me in a couple of days,' Lauren was saying. 'Maybe I can slip something in with the blood work or the prints or something. But not today. I'm sorry.'

Not many supervisors would be caught saying they were sorry, Jilly reflected as she hung up. Lauren was a special one indeed.

She opened her notebook and perused her notes from earlier in the day. Still another canvass had been conducted throughout the neighborhoods around Parker and San Mateo Streets in search of the true identity of the street person, Mary — for some reason, she and Dan had started to refer to her as Mary X, as if they were uncomfortable with the indignity of her not having a real name or that she had simply become 'the bag lady' or 'the street lady.' They both hated departmental terminologies, like 'DB' for dead body or 'Jane Doe' for anonymous victims.

Early on in their partnership, Jilly had discovered that Dan shared her distaste for such depersonalizations. She might have become inured to the harsh realities of her nightly world but she refused to forget that every single tragedy and abomination was still ultimately a human one. They were people, most of them had loved ones and friends as well, and somehow she knew that the day she forgot that was the day she would begin to lose her own humanity.

She had carried around a photo of the unidentified dead woman, taken at the morgue. It was stark but it was all they had.

She knocked on doors, stopped individuals on the street and in the stores, inquired of bus and cab drivers. Nobody could identify her. Mary X remained an enigma.

Jilly knew she would return tomorrow at some opportune moment and try again, and Dan had volunteered to do the same.

Turning her attention back to the searches she had been pursuing, she closed the open windows on her computer screen and sighed. As far as she could ascertain, the Little Command didn't seem to exist any more.

Paulinho Silva was presumed dead, since nothing had been heard from him for almost nine years. There was no new information on members of the splinter group or the man who had led them, or on any of his former lieutenants.

They had all descended into obscurity — a common enough fate for criminal figures with misguided pretensions to power. The scene and the cast of characters in the Rio underworld appeared to have moved on with the times.

As far as Jilly could tell from earlier phone conversations with experts in global organized crime, the Red Command was a local, almost insular, concern, concentrating most of its efforts on its dealings in Rio.

It had tenuous organizational connections in Colombia and one or two other South American nations but did not extend into the United States in any significant way, nor did it seem to have alliances with other organizations that might.

It seemed far-fetched to think that after so many years and so much water under the bridge, the cartel would have either dispatched its own hit man, or contracted for the murder of a relative of a long-deceased rival.

Of course it was not totally off the table just yet. A personal vendetta could have burned within some criminal heart. The Colombians might have connections here, and there might be a link to the Red Command, but the idea struck Jilly as awfully flimsy.

She considered the Ricky Wright angle. Not much had come up on him either. He was a minor player or, more likely, just a wannabe. No serious brushes with the law — nothing violent, no weapons, no felonies. He was only known on the street to the extent that he was seen all the time in clubs and similar hangouts. No apparent aspirations to an extra-legal career of any kind.

He seemed to concentrate on making time with his many girlfriends and concocting various fantasies about his so-called music business career.

Jilly kept running a scenario through her head with minor variations: Ricky finds out about Marina's secret past. He tries to ingratiate himself with some 'connected' character who might in turn have influence in the music business — or maybe it was as simple as just gaining access to some intriguing young woman, by passing on the info.

It gets back to someone who gives the go-ahead for an opportunistic killing. And, perhaps not coincidentally, Ricky gets taken out as well, thus cleaning up all the loose ends.

But there was something about the theory she just did not like. Instinctively she felt it didn't make sense.

During her forays back to the bar, she had encountered a good number of people who casually knew Ricky, but nobody had ever seen him in the company of gangsters or the like.

He did aspire to be a music industry player, and perhaps that was the connection, as unlikely as it seemed. She had to continue to consider this avenue, long shot though it might be.

And she had to keep a guard on Jané and her husband until she could be sure — or as long as the strained Department would let her keep one on her.

Ricky was a true riddle. He hung out with lots of people but there didn't seem to be a single close friend who actually knew him. No family had yet turned up. She'd have to keep asking, keep looking.

For a lot of reasons, Jilly hoped this would turn out to be a false trail. It was just too complicated, and there were too many bad possibilities if it did turn out to be true.

She got on the phone to Dan. 'Hey partner, when you're done with your current follow-up on your stabbing, how would you feel about looking into some angles on our friend Ricky Wright?'

* * *

The foreman on the loading dock at Builders Depot was a burly, hirsute guy named, appropriately enough, Harry. He was in the middle of orchestrating several ongoing tasks but when he saw the proffered detective's shield, he put down his clipboard with an air of resignation and turned his attention to Frank.

'I'll tell you what I told the other guy, Rudy ain't been here today.'

Frank put his hands on his hips and stared. 'And what other guy would that be?'

'The other detective. Younger Asian guy?'

'Detective Lee.'

'Yeah, that's the one. I already told him. Rudy never came to work today. Probably still sleeping it off. Don't you guys talk to each other?'

'Humor me for a minute,' Frank said. 'How long has Rudy worked here?'

'Maybe three years. Used to be the foreman on the dock here. Good worker . . . ' Harry trailed off as if he was going to continue but then thought better of it.

'You were going to say a good worker except . . . ?'

' . . . Yeah. Good man, when he's . . . well, sober.'

'So Rudy's got a bit of a problem with the drinking?'

'Now and then. More lately. So what'd he do anyway, if it isn't out of line asking?'

Frank sidestepped the question. 'Was he at work Thursday?'

'Until I sent him home. He was tipsy, to say the least. Before lunch.'

'Is that usual for Rudy?'

'Lately he's been bent outa shape about something. I think it's his wife. Something at home. Whatever, I told him he wasn't good for anything, told him to clock out and go home.

'He said something about there being nothing at home for him anymore. Probably went and had a few more. So he went and got himself in some kinda trouble, it sounds like?'

'Himself and a few other people. Violent guy?'

'When he's sober, naw, he's a pussycat. Probably lets people walk over him too much in fact.

'When he drinks he gets a little touchy. Still not violent, exactly, just a little sensitive? It's like he's got a line, and as long as someone doesn't cross it . . . '

Harry seemed reluctant to volunteer too much more information.

'Hey, look, Detective, I'm sorry, but as you can see, there's a lot going on here right now, and I've already talked to that other detective . . . '

'I don't think Detective Lee mentioned that Rudy is dead,' Frank said. That stopped Harry in his tracks. 'And may have taken a couple of people with him. So how about I take a little more of your time . . . ?'

* * *

When Dan Lee had first made detective, he could have been assigned as a partner to several experienced colleagues, but he well appreciated that he had lucked out being paired with Jilly Garvey. One of the other possibilities could have been Detective Marlon Morrison, and as he sat talking with the man now, he reflected on his good fortune. Morrison was a weathered veteran but there was something about him that definitely rubbed Dan the wrong way.

138

'Ricky Wright. Sure, I've heard the name.'

'Anything specifically come to mind with him?'

Morrison shrugged. 'Not really. Minor street hustler type of guy. There's dozens of 'em.'

'Any chance he could have been involved with anything more serious? Drug dealers, that type of thing?'

Morrison scrunched in his chair, looking bored and impatient. He waved a hand. 'Nothing comes to mind.'

'So how do you know him? Ever arrest him?'

'I think I questioned him about a robbery last year. Yeah, that's it. Holdup of a club.

'Couple guys got shot. No deaths. Wright was one of the people there. I think he was with the DJ. He seemed a little off but, at least that I could establish, he didn't seem involved. Never came to arrest or charges or anything of that nature. I still think he might have had something to do with it.'

Dan's interest was piqued. 'Why's that?'

'Well, we figured there was an insider,

so to speak, someone who knew when and where there would be cash? Wright was one of the guys who seemed to know the club owners and workers. Nothing substantial.'

'Ever find the perps?'

'Nope.'

Big surprise, Dan thought. Morrison had a reputation for putting in the minimal effort lately. He was coasting to his anticipated retirement. Still, he had been around a long time and if anybody in the squad room would know something it would likely be him.

'Any chance that this involved anyone from out of town or out of the country? Drug cartels, syndicates, anything like that? Some kind of grudge maybe?'

'Doubt it. Couple, three punks decided to knock over a club. We looked at regular patrons, business associates of the owners, that kind of thing. Thought maybe there'd be some word out after the fact, but no luck.'

'What kind of business associates did this club involve?'

'The usual. There's always somebody

unsavory back there. Low-level types. This wasn't like a mobbed-up establishment; there's not a lot of that anyway, and even then you'd have to be crazy to try to rob a connected joint.'

'So there's no way you can see that Ricky Wright would have had some connection to anything, uh, above his station?'

'Above his station. Nice way to put it, Lee, you got a way with a word. Not that I could see. He's just a dime a dozen hustler. Not the brightest one either.'

'But you *do* think he might have had something to do with that particular robbery?'

Morrison shrugged again. 'Maybe yes, maybe no. Couldn't prove anything.'

'So where was this club and who were the owners?' Dan asked, reaching for his notebook. He quietly felt relieved that this conversation was coming to a conclusion.

★   ★   ★

The club was called Selena, after its highest-profile owner, Selena Chance.

141

Dan doubted she was a majority owner by any means, but she was a perfect choice for the face of the establishment.

She was in her late thirties, personable and highly attractive, a local performer and minor celebrity, and her patrons in general were delighted to interact with her.

It was fairly late by the time Dan was able to get to the club and the music, dancing and partying were in full swing.

He had to wait while she tended to her proprietorial duties, making the rounds with her customers and dealing with matters at hand.

She finally greeted him and led him up the staircase past a mirrored bar to an office containing a small desk, and photos on the walls of Selena with various notables.

The room was reasonably insulated from the noise of the club, and only a vague muffled thump of bass could be heard intermittently behind the closed doors.

She motioned for Dan to have a seat and offered him a drink, which he passed up with a wave of a hand.

'So how may I help you?' she said with a disarming smile, gracefully seating herself across from him. Dan got right to business.

'Are you familiar with Ricky Wright?'

'Sure, I knew him. I heard what happened. Terrible thing.'

'What was his connection to this club?'

'He didn't really have one, not officially. He hung out here now and then. He knew my DJs. I think he liked to associate with anybody who had anything to do with the music business.'

'So he was in the music business himself?'

Selena raised her eyebrows. 'I think he *wanted* to be, do you know what I mean? Ricky really wanted to be a part of that scene. He liked to tell people he was involved in recording deals, things like that.'

'But you don't think he was actually in the business.'

Selena shook her head with a knowing smile. 'Ricky was a wannabe. He picked up girls with lines like that, tried to impress certain guys. Most of them saw through his stories. Now and then he'd score with someone not quite so wise to things.'

'It doesn't sound like you thought much of him.'

'Oh, Ricky was a sweet enough guy, Detective, uh . . . what was your name?'

'Lee. Detective Lee.'

'Of course, forgive me. Ricky could be very charming and very amusing. He was likable enough, and he was kind of handsome, in his way.

'But he could also be tiresome, if you get my meaning. A lot of people got bored with him. Or fed up.'

'Sounds like maybe you were one of them. How exactly do you mean fed up?'

'Well, Ricky tended to overstep his bounds. He could be overly familiar with people and sometimes they were the wrong people.' She hesitated a moment as if considering what she was about to say.

'He would hit on women indiscriminately, even if they were far out of his league, do you know?'

The implication was clear that Selena was one of them. But this was an intriguing new possibility.

'So Ricky may have made overtures to the wrong young woman, perhaps somebody's girlfriend or wife?'

'Oh, he got set straight on that score a few times, yes.'

'Could he ever have pushed the boundary too far, earned a grudge from the wrong person?'

Selena laughed. 'It's not out of the question, I suppose. But Ricky was the type to charm his way out of a confrontation, or in any case back off. He wasn't the bravest guy.

'Once or twice he did get things explained to him a bit physically. He got the message and moved on.'

Still, Dan considered, this idea was something worth pursuing, maybe.

'So Ricky wanted to be a major player. Were there patrons here that he might have especially admired or tried to emulate?'

'Probably quite a few. We have a rather high-profile clientele. A number of music and entertainment industry figures. Ricky would always try to play up to any of them he could.'

'Was there anybody in particular you

can think of that he especially wanted to impress?'

'The guy he made the biggest play for was Neil Cassara. With Tech-Now Entertainment?'

She raised her eyebrows, expecting instant recognition. Dan drew a blank.

'Ricky would have loved to get a foot in that door. He made himself a bit of a nuisance. We had to step in and suggest he stop bothering Neil.' She shook her head.

'That was the one time I had to have a talk with Ricky and set him straight. Kind of like a restraining order. After that he didn't bother Neil anymore.'

She smiled sweetly at her own joke and Dan couldn't help smiling as well.

'But I don't want to give the impression Ricky was too much of a problem. This is a club, people drink, dance, let off steam. We allow a certain leeway within reasonable limits. Usually he behaved and observed those limits. He enjoyed himself and everything stayed cool.'

'I understand there was an incident here last year?'

'The robbery, yeah.' She rolled her eyes. 'Unfortunate. It was late afternoon, not too many people in the place. No bouncers stationed at the door yet. Some guys came in, followed the manager into the back office — the bigger one — pulled guns and demanded the take.

'It happened to be just before the regular cash pickup. We have a service that comes by in an armored car on a timely basis, but at irregular periods.'

'So it's not precisely predictable,' Dan interjected.

'Exactly.'

'But the thieves seemed to know when this was going to happen?'

'The police certainly thought so. It was curious.'

'How many robbers? Were they masked?'

'Three. At least three went into the office. No masks, nothing. Our accountant was back there tallying the money when they entered. They had him put the money into some bags they pulled out. The manager and the accountant cooperated, nobody was going to get hurt, it seemed. It all took about five minutes

— that is, until they came back out.'

'Then what happened?'

'One of our security guys, Trask, figured out what was happening. He hit the alarm and drew his own gun at the bottom of the stairs.

'There were some shots exchanged, people running for cover and screaming. Nobody, it would seem, was a great shot.

'Trask and another employee got hit. They both got taken to the ER and recovered. The gunmen got away in the excitement. The wall caught a couple of bullets, a mirror got shattered. Cops finally showed up' — Dan caught the dig — 'that was that.'

'There was some thought there was an insider, someone who maybe kept their eyes and ears open and knew about the cash?'

'That was explored, without much success. You're not thinking Ricky had anything to do with that?' Selena seemed genuinely surprised at the prospect.

'Is it possible?'

She bit her lower lip and thought for a moment, then shook her head. 'I don't see it. I just don't.' She left it at that.

Perhaps he was still developing his investigative instincts, but it struck Dan as just a bit insincere. He wished that Jilly could have been here as well, to compare notes on this.

'You're not the only owner, is that correct?'

'That's right. There are two others.'

'And who are they?'

'Lowell and Tony Michaels.'

The names meant nothing to Dan. 'Either one of them present tonight?'

'No, they're usually here during the day taking care of matters at hand. They're sometimes here in the evenings but in general I'm the presence when the club is in full swing.'

'So the best time to speak with them would be during the afternoon?'

'You could likely catch one of them around most days, yes. But it's not guaranteed. The head manager, Sergio, is more likely to be on the premises.'

He threw out the loaded question, not really expecting a truthful answer.

Were there ever, to her knowledge, any

underworld-related figures connected to or in attendance at the club?

She expressed the expected shock at the very question. Of course not. She seemed just a bit less forthcoming thereafter. He inwardly chastised himself for even asking — or at least for not waiting until the very end to ask.

Dan explored a few more avenues with her, none of which seemed overly promising.

Finally there was a pause in the conversation and Selena looked up expectantly and said, 'If there isn't anything else, I really should get back.'

Dan replied that he thought he had covered everything for the moment and stood up. He remembered to leave her a card and fumbled in his pocket for one, handing it to her as she also rose from her seat.

She gave him a smile and a handshake and escorted him out into the blare of the club.

On the street, returning to his car, Dan considered the options. Ricky Wright, an unimpressive man apparently desperate to impress. He wanted to be part of whatever was going on. Clearly he had a big ego, a big mouth, and bad judgment.

He could have given the word on the cash in the club to someone who followed through on the robbery — or maybe he was just suspected of it. Either way there could have been a similar result.

Was there a payback?

The entertainment big shot that Ricky was harassing was another avenue. Maybe Ricky continued to overstep his boundaries outside the club.

Two possibilities: One, the guy was connected and somehow Ricky pushed him way too far. Or alternately, Ricky blabbed something in an effort to impress him. If the guy was connected maybe someone else overheard the conversation. Too many avenues opening up. He needed to sit down with Jilly and sort this out.

* * *

'So what've we got?' Dan asked, flopping into his chair.

Jilly leaned across her cluttered desk and sighed deeply and without delight.

It had been a long day trying to hit as many objectives as they could, and finally they had reunited here in the squad room.

They were hardly the only ones overburdened at the moment. Despite the late hour, detectives, clericals, and uniformed personnel bustled back and forth around them, everyone looking distracted, on their own mission, oblivious to everything else.

'Not a blessed lot, Dan, and then again maybe way too much. Tell me about your day first.'

'Well, like you suspected, Ricky Wright might be a can of worms. He seems to have indiscriminately opened his mouth a lot. He might have been involved in a club robbery, and there might have been some phantom owners of that club who didn't like it.'

'That sounds like a lot of 'if's,' Jilly sighed. 'And he still might have divulged something about Marina to someone who told someone.

'We still don't even know which one of them was the intended victim. I tried to trace down any possible connection there today without any luck.

'And I spent another couple of hours around the Parker and San Mateo area in search of our friend Mary X. Not a blessed soul seems to have known her.'

'Not much on Tia either. She's a mystery woman as well. No family to speak of. Nobody seems to know where she worked, or anything like that. Her husband seems to have disappeared too. I've been chasing ghosts all day.'

'Lovely,' muttered Jilly. 'Lucky us.'

A shadow fell across the papers scattered all over Dan's desk and someone cleared his throat. Dan looked up, and Jilly looked over her shoulder.

Frank Vandegraf stood there, hands in pockets, looking tired and pensive as always. 'I think we should talk,' he said quietly.

8

'So Tia Carlisle was stabbed to death by her husband Rudy,' Dan was saying, looking at the scribbled note cards they had spread around his desk, 'who found out she was cheating on him with this car salesman guy.'

'But first I'm thinking Rudy killed Al Land,' Frank added. 'But that one's a bit of a puzzle.

'Rudy was financially strapped. Possibly someone paid him to take out Al, but now I'm more inclined to believe it was a case of mistaken identity. Rudy just doesn't strike me as the assassin type.

'The car salesman's vehicle was parked right in front of the bar. Both guys were wearing leather jackets. Maybe all Rudy saw was Tia getting into Lowell's SUV, but only got a glimpse of the guy, and followed them.

'He walks into the bar next to the car, sees a guy about the same build as

Lowell, there are two drinks on the table and his companion is in, er, the loo, and he figures he's got the right guy. What I don't understand is why he would reach in and take Al's Glock.'

'And why didn't he wait for Tia to come out, if he thought it was Tia, and plug her too?' said Jilly.

'Probably scared. He couldn't have been thinking too straight. Sounds like he was pretty ripped and through the wringer.'

'So he takes off and Land's wife chases him,' Dan added.

'Apparently she takes a potshot at him,' Frank said. 'But I got her gun and it *hadn't* been fired.'

'So she's got two guns?' Jilly said.

'Conceivably,' said Frank, remembering his failure to follow up on that in Saint Expedito when he suddenly had to move on.

'Or, there's one other possibility. I'll need to discuss that with Anita, after Al's services.'

'Apparently at some point Rudy catches sight of Lowell and Tia in the SUV and realizes he's made a big mistake,' Jilly continued.

'There's a bullet hole in the passenger's-side door of Lowell's car,' Frank said. 'Maybe something like this happened: Lowell drops Tia off at the quickie mart where she picks up some items she decides she needs.

'Rudy pulls up and takes a potshot at him, Lowell panics and drives off. Rudy gets out of the car and comes after Tia, just coming out of the store. She sees him and runs.'

'Rudy uses a knife instead of his gun?' Dan asked.

'Maybe he leaves it in the car, not thinking. Or maybe . . . ' Frank was pensive for a long moment, working it out. 'Maybe he needed to reload and there wasn't time.'

'Two bullets in Land, one in Lowell's car,' Dan said. 'Five shots in the .38 if it's fully loaded. What about the rest?'

'Let's wait. We'll come back to that,' Frank said. 'I bet the blood on the knife in Rudy's truck and on the hoodie matches Tia's.

'He takes her wallet and some other stuff, maybe to make it look like a robbery, maybe to make it harder to identify her, whatever. Maybe he just grabs it reflexively. We know he's not thinking too straight at this point. Anyway, he gets back in the truck, strips off his bloody jacket, and takes off to find Lowell. Lowell is still his primary objective.'

'And he finds him in that scuzzy parking lot,' Jilly said grimly, pushing the cards around very slowly, as if they were actual human lives she was manipulating. 'And if he needed to reload, he must have, since then he takes Lowell out with the gun.'

'Lowell was in the process of calling Tia on his cell phone when Rudy found him,' Frank said. 'He had her on his speed dial and had started the call.

'He might have stopped in the lot to calm down, take stock, contact her then figure out what to do next.'

'If this is what happened,' Jilly added, 'at this point Lowell would have no idea what had happened to Tia. Maybe he wouldn't have quite put it all together in his head yet? He might not have realized it was Rudy coming after him. He might not even have known what Rudy actually looked like!'

'A lot of *if*s,' Dan said with a shake of his head. 'I don't know.'

'When the ballistics and the DNA come back I gotta believe it's all gonna match up,' Frank muttered, rubbing his mouth with a hand.

'So then what happened to Rudy?' Dan asked. 'Just randomly hit, or was someone taking him out?'

'Another person involved in all this?' Jilly asked.

'Accidental hit-and-run seems a remarkable coincidence,' Frank admitted. 'And I still haven't found the Glock anywhere.'

Jilly picked up the thread as Frank's voice tailed off. 'So maybe there's some connection with this D'Yquem guy . . . or one of Al's numerous other fervent admirers?'

'I can't dismiss it just yet,' Frank allowed.

'Well, anyway,' said Dan, 'at least one of our DBs — excuse me, one of our victims — is looking good. If only we could catch a break on the others.'

Frank looked at him for a long time. 'Tell me about them,' he said. 'I have a feeling there's a lot more to Thursday night's story.'

★ ★ ★

'That vermin is dead, you say?' Cassandra Washington said without a drop of remorse, feigned or otherwise. 'Cannot say as I am sorry.'

'He was under investigation for allegedly threatening you,' Frank said, watching her as he spoke.

They were sitting at a remote table in a coffee shop. She was a slight wispy woman, perhaps forty, unsmiling, dressed in a collar-up trench coat and sunglasses. Frightened, figured Frank . . . and trying to stay incognito.

'Allegedly my foot,' she spat. 'The louse was calling me in the middle of the night telling me bad things were going to happen if we didn't retract our suit against DKM.

'The guy thinks he's some kind of spy commando or something. I remember reading about that guy who worked for Nixon who lived in a tough-guy dream world? That was what Al Land was like. What a jerk. How did he die?'

'Shot at close range.' Frank kept his eye on her. There was a short silence. She sipped her latté from the cardboard cup and nodded as if it made sense.

'I was so happy when the indictments came down on him. I figured maybe we'd all be safe now.'

'Did the threats stop?'

'Who knows for how long, but yes, they did. You're thinking one of us involved in the lawsuits shot him?'

Frank shrugged. 'Just looking at everything.'

'This guy was a real piece of work, Detective. I've no doubt he consorted with a lot of scary people and he mouthed off at all of them, I'm sure.

'But he was a bully at heart. The kind of people he and D'Yquem's thugs liked to threaten were like me, people he could put a scare into and who wouldn't fight back.'

Frank waited a while before answering.

160

'Maybe somebody finally decided they'd had enough and weren't going to take it anymore.'

Her turn to shrug. 'Maybe. I was happy to let the law step in. We were all in way over our heads. We should never have made any deals with D'Yquem to begin with. What did we know? Lambs to the slaughter . . . '

'This was a very high-profile lawsuit.'

'Sure.'

'Anybody, maybe, under the radar?'

'I don't get you, Detective.'

'I mean, do you know of somebody Al messed with who *didn't* stand to be protected by the lawsuit or the indictment? Somebody a little more — '

'Criminal?' Cassandra finished, pinching the corners of her mouth. 'In this particular case, I can't think of anybody like that. But as I said — he slept with dogs. He must have gotten a lot of fleas.'

*   *   *

As distasteful as it was to Dan, another conversation with Marlon Morrison seemed the easiest way to at least get started, and so there they sat in the squad room with matching cups of coffee.

'You said you thought there might be some shadow nightclub owners backing Selena, right? These Michaels brothers, maybe just beards or fronts?'

'It's conceivable.' Morrison yawned, showing little to no interest in the subject. 'But don't try to read too much into that. Sometimes it's just a matter of someone wanting to stay out of the spotlight.

'Maybe they don't want to be publicly associated with the enterprise. Or maybe they're someone who for whatever reason would have trouble obtaining a license for the joint. I doubt the place is mobbed up, not in a major way.'

'How about a guy named Neil Cassara? He owns something called Tech-Now Entertainment?'

'Oh sure, everybody knows him. Major player. Music, films, gaming, all sorts of stuff. You don't read the papers? I guess a young guy like you is more an internet type, but still. Watch TV?'

'Not a lot of any of those,' Dan

admitted. 'So tell me about this guy Cassara.'

'He's like what you'd call a mogul. All sorts of deals, works out of Hollywood and New York and other places. He's got homes all over, jets around, but he grew up here and keeps a big old mansion up on the river.'

'Any chance this guy is connected?'

Morrison made a raspberry sound. 'Back to the mobbed-up stuff again. I'm telling you, forget that angle, Lee.'

'Okay, but if he's a mogul, like you say, he's not exactly a choir boy, right? If a guy sufficiently ticked him off, isn't it possible someone close to him might have taken it upon themselves to remedy the situation?'

Morrison raised his hands in exasperation. 'Something you're going to learn here, Detective, is that the simplest answer is more often the right one. You're looking for conspiracies.'

And you, Dan thought as he stood up, *are used to looking for the easiest way out.* He headed across the room for the computer he shared with Jilly.

★ ★ ★

As expected, neither of the Michaels brothers was present at Selena when Dan showed up. The place was empty except for a small crew of bartenders, waiters, and other employees, busily setting up for the evening.

He was directed back to the small office at the top of the stairs once again, where he found Sergio, the lead manager.

He was a husky nervous sort, and definitely not the sociable kind. He looked put out by Dan's intrusion but once he saw the badge and ID, he put aside his papers and sat down to talk.

Dan opened with a few routine questions about the earlier robbery and some inquiries about Ricky Wright.

Sergio said that he had indeed been the manager confronted by the gunmen and forced to take them upstairs to the office. He claimed he didn't know Ricky.

'How long have you been with this club?'

'I've been employed here almost five years now. I've been lead manager for the past two or so.'

'What can you tell me about the Michaels brothers, the co-owners?'

Sergio shrugged. 'What's there to tell?'

'Well, I'm not familiar with them. Did they start this place?'

'Yeah, they were the original proprietors. They brought Selena in. She was a local celeb, they knew she'd be a great draw, so they offered her a share and named the club after her. It was a brilliant move. The rest is history.'

'So where did they get their money from? Starting a place like this has to be expensive.'

More shrugs. 'I dunno, I think they're like investment brokers or something of the sort, something in the financial world. They were more interested in running this as a sideline, not a main source of revenue.'

Dan flipped through the notes he had made prior to coming to the club. He spoke while perusing them.

'They don't seem to spend much time here. Not all that much interested in day to day operations, apparently.'

'Tony's usually here a couple days a week. Lowell is on the move a lot, with his other business. I do most of the grunt work.'

'Any chance there are any other, what you might call silent partners, involved in the ownership here?'

'What do you mean? There's Tony, there's Lowell, there's Selena. That's it.'

'No,' Dan said, looking up. 'There's someone else. The original investment in the startup was pretty substantial. The return is pretty substantial as well.

'I have a feeling if the numbers were to be looked into closely, for instance the Michaels brothers' accounts, it wouldn't add up. You've got two main investors supposedly totally uninterested in a place that they hardly ever come to. Come on, Sergio.' He winked. 'You can tell me.'

'I don't know what you're talking about,' Sergio said blankly. 'Everything is on the up and up here, Detective. What you see is what you got.'

*   *   *

'So what's up, Officer Pardo?' They were standing in the same parking lot once

166

again, this time with the sun slowly dying in the sky.

Frank's afternoon of chasing down whistle-blowers had not been fruitful. He was hoping for something, anything, to make his day. The officer had her notebook out and was flipping through pages diligently.

'Thank you for coming out here, Detective. I think I might have something for you on that bludgeoning. As I told you the other day, there are a group of guys who hang out in this lot fairly regularly, maybe buy some motor oil in the Ready Rite for their cars and change it out here in the lot, brown-bag a beer, things like that.

'Big gearheads, really into their cars. Mostly young men we sometimes bust for underage drinking or loitering. I came by earlier today to talk to them.'

'You're not going to tell me somebody gave up Sonny Foster's killer, I assume,' Frank said.

'No sir. Nobody saw anything, nobody knows anything. None of them were even here the other night, even though they were, if you follow me. What we *did* notice, however, was who *wasn't* there.'

'Come again, Officer?'

'There's one kid who hasn't been around the last couple of days. He's almost always out here. But nobody's seen him and nobody knows anything about him all of a sudden.'

'Who is this kid?'

'Luther Newcombe. They call him Newk. He's like eighteen, nineteen years old. Drives a green tricked-out old Mustang.'

'Hmm.'

'And as you know, Detective, there was green paint from the collision where Rudy Caliente was hit.'

'Yes, Officer Pardo, I recall.' Frank rubbed the back of his neck and looked around. 'Got any other info on this 'Newk' guy?'

'Had his driver's license run.' There was a slip of paper stuck into her notebook that she handed him.

'Officer,' Frank said, taking the paper, 'someday when you make detective, remind me to come congratulate you and say I saw it coming. Thank you.'

For the moment she couldn't stay entirely decorous and smiled and blushed despite herself.

9

The Newcombe address was a small house in an older working-class neighborhood. Nobody answered the doorbell and there didn't seem to be anybody at home.

There were no cars parked out front, green Mustang or otherwise. There was a small windowless garage adjacent to the house, locked up tight.

He knocked on neighbors' doors and had no better luck, though he did detect a slight flutter of curtains in one window. He decided to try back later — or perhaps send some uniforms over to pick the kid up.

★   ★   ★

'Yeah, I've known Rudy for a long time. We went to high school together. Went fishing together a lot. Rudy loved to fish especially.'

Tommy Nathanson was a tall, dark-complexioned, youthfully good-looking

170

guy. 'This is terrible what happened to him. Any idea who hit him?'

'Working on it,' Frank said. They were sitting together in the break room of the copy shop where Tommy worked, two half-full Styrofoam cups of dreadful coffee in front of them.

'Rudy had some problems lately, didn't he?'

Tommy shook his head sadly. 'Yeah. You know, he's one of the nicest guys you could hope to meet, just a really good guy, but when he gets to drinking . . . man, everything just went down the drain for him.'

'I hear he got demoted at his job.'

'Yeah, he had money hassles, and he was starting to worry about his wife. He thought she was seeing some other guy.'

'Tell me about that.'

'Not much to tell. He figured she was seeing this guy with more money than him, a nicer car, that kind of stuff. He really cared for her. He used to say how lucky he was he had found her. It was eating him up.'

'So he was spending a lot of time in the bar, maybe doing other things?'

Tommy nodded. 'To be honest, he was getting pretty messed up. I was worried about the guy. Tried to get him to go fishing with me, maybe get away from all this, but he just kept getting deeper into his blue, you know what I mean?'

'Did he say if he planned to do anything?'

'Yeah, he was talking about running this guy down — I mean, finding him, that's all — and having it out with him.'

'Did you see him the day he got killed?'

'Oh yeah. We were in Worthy's, over on Main. He got sent home from his job. He'd had a few. I had to head to work myself, but I told him he should go home and sleep it off. He told me he was going to do that. I made him promise. Guess he didn't do that.'

Frank rubbed the back of his neck. 'Is there any chance Rudy would have been looking to make some money on the side, maybe doing something less than legal?'

'You mean like dealing or something?'

'I was thinking more like hurting someone.'

'Aw, no way, Detective. No way. Rudy

172

wasn't a violent guy. We went hunting a coupla times and even though he liked to hunt, he wasn't even any good at that. He was pretty gentle. He just couldn't have hurt someone. There's no way he could have put someone into pain for money.'

'Rudy shot two people,' Frank said. 'And he stabbed his wife. They're all dead.'

Tommy gazed back a Frank, stunned, taking all this in. 'There's no way.'

'There is, I'm afraid. It's true.'

'This had to have been a, what do you call it, a crime of passion. There's no way Rudy Caliente was a cold-blooded killer.'

'Have you ever heard of a guy named Al Land?'

'Nope. Who is he?'

'One of the people Rudy killed. He had a lot of enemies but seems to have been a stranger to Rudy. You don't think someone would have hired Rudy to take him out, and then turned around and killed Rudy?'

'Detective, you are describing someone totally unlike Rudy. No way.' He sat thinking for a long time before speaking again. 'Rudy was pretty turned around over Tia. Was this Land guy her boyfriend?'

'No, that would seem to be the other guy he killed. Land didn't seem to have any connection to the situation.'

'It's a stretch, a real stretch, but . . . I could see how Rudy might have killed Tia and her boyfriend if things just sorta happened. This other guy — I got no idea. It makes no sense that Rudy would kill for hire. It's just not him. No freaking way.'

★   ★   ★

Frank had been sitting at his table for a long time, mulling it all over for still another time. He wanted it to be the simple explanation.

Rudy had shot Al Land out of mistaken identity. But he had to be sure. Too many people had it in for Land. And someone had gone to the trouble to tie up the loose ends and take out Rudy.

It made things way too complicated. He had to cover the doubt. Maybe he was going to have to go back to those lovely folks at DKM again. He definitely was going to have to talk with Anita again. And there was still the matter, which had almost slipped his mind, of sending someone over to look for Luther Newcombe.

The phone on his desk rang.

'Detective, this is Mallory, down at the desk. There's somebody here needs to talk to you.'

Luther Newcombe was tall for his age. He could have been any kind of a martini, Frank mused, since he seemed both shaken and stirred. Sitting on either side of him in the interview room across the table were his stern, prematurely-graying father and his slightly-built mother, her eyes wide and filled with tears.

'I've been doing my term in the Middle East,' Lawrence Newcombe was telling Frank. 'Only got back a couple of months ago. Couldn't be here for my son but I've got to be here for him now. I told him this was the only thing to do.'

'And it's the right thing, Mr. Newcombe. I appreciate that. I know this can't be easy for any of you.'

'Took me a couple of days to convince him to come in with me. It was all an accident. Boy didn't mean to hurt no one, you got to realize that.'

Frank nodded and looked at Luther.

'Sonny and me got into it,' Luther said quietly, hesitantly, not looking up from the table. 'He's a lot bigger and tougher'n me and he used to give me a lot of . . . ' he glanced at his mother ' . . . the business, you know? This time I decided to stand up to him and he started punchin' me around.

'He was twisting my arm behind my back and callin' me some things, you know? Personal, insulting things? In front of everybody and everything. All I wanted was for him to stop. I grabbed this bar lyin' near me on the ground and whacked him with it, 'cross the head. He let go of me. I guess I hit him a coupla times. I was p'd off.'

'Mind the language in front of your mother,' his father interrupted.

'Sorry. I was mad, is what I meant. Guess I hit him pretty hard. I got scared and when he let me go I ran for my car.

All I wanted to do was get away from there. I didn't even see the other guy. I hit him, musta run him over, smacked into a couple of other cars in the lot, and just got out of there. I didn't even know I had killed either one of them until I saw it on TV.'

'He's not a bad boy,' Lawrence Newcombe said solemnly, putting his arm around his son's shoulders. 'He was scared. He shouldn't have run. Now he needs to do the right thing.'

Frank made some notes on the pad in front of him.

'Well, he's done the right thing, Mr. Newcombe, and I thank you all for that.'

'He's got to take the responsibility for this, Detective, but isn't there something you can do for him?'

'We'll see,' Frank said. 'I'll do what I can.'

'Bad night all around,' Luther murmured quietly. 'I should never 'a gone out at all.'

'Lotta people shouldn't have gone out,' Frank agreed, 'that particular night.'

★ ★ ★

'Still looking over that map?' Dan asked. Frank, bent over the desk perusing an unfolded map of the city, glanced up at him.

'So where's Jilly?'

His desk had been cleared of the usual clutter and completely covered by the spread-out map. Frank had used a red marker to put big spots on the crime scenes of that evening.

'She's around. What've you got?'

'Bear with me here,' he said. 'Just a thought.'

He began running his finger, street to street, while he talked, bringing his finger down with some emphasis on the various red dots. Saint Expedito. Parker and San Mateo. Las Candilejas. Webley. The Ready Rite.

Jilly had mysteriously appeared at some point behind Frank's right shoulder.

Neither man had noticed until she exclaimed, 'Are you kidding me?'

Frank looked over his shoulder at her. 'Maybe it's all a stretch, but it fits. And it

178

pretty much covers everything. You got anything better?'

Jilly and Dan looked at one another for a long time, and she started to walk away.

'Where you going?'

'To my phone. I'm sure they haven't gotten to the ballistics tests yet. Better add a couple more.'

'Frank,' Dan said, carefully inspecting the map, silently replaying the earlier narration as he trailed a finger over the route, 'this is screwed up enough to be right.'

'I wasn't sure until a little while ago. Now I'm starting to convince myself.'

'If the ballistics and the labs all come back right . . . '

'Whenever that's going to happen,' Frank said, grimacing. 'Meanwhile, I guess there's one more conversation I've still got to have.'

10

'How was the service, Anita?' They were sitting on the balcony of the hillside condo Al and Anita had owned for several years.

It had a view of the far-off harbor. It was a chilly, overcast day but neither of them seemed to mind.

Anita shrugged. 'Okay, I guess. Not too many people. DKM sent a few guys. The minister got a couple things wrong. Guess that's what comes of not being a churchgoer . . . when you die, there's no clergyman to remember you right.'

Frank nodded without comment. Al wasn't exactly a man with a lot of friends. But he wouldn't have been surprised at a lot of ornate Godfather-like crocodile-tear sendoffs from the people who wished they had done the job instead. People like Billy Wilde or Duane Scudder.

They talked for a few more minutes about minutiae. The service. Anita's plans for the condo. Finally she put down her coffee cup and looked Frank straight in the eye.

'So thanks for the condolences and all, but what's really on your mind, Detective?'

Frank looked at her long and hard before saying it outright.

'So do you still have Al's gun, Anita?'

She returned his stare, just as steady.

'That nut job who shot him took it, you know that. So you never found it?'

'Nope. Funny thing about that. Just about everything else in the world in that guy's car, but no Glock.'

More awkward silence accompanying unbroken stares. It was like one of those games kids play to see who blinks first.

Finally Frank continued. 'Someone saw you taking a shot at Rudy as he drove away. You didn't fire your own gun — you were nice enough to hand that over to me right away to demonstrate that fact. You shot another gun . . . Al's. You grabbed it from his holster when you ran to him.'

Anita still said nothing.

'You know, GSR lasts a long time,

Anita. We can still test you.'

'And gunshot residue will show that I fired a gun recently? So what? I'm a danged PI. I go to the firing range two, three times a week.'

'Cut it, Anita.' The staring contest continued.

It was Anita who broke the spell, picking up her coffee cup and sighing before taking a decidedly unladylike swig to empty it.

'I don't have Al's gun, Detective.'

'So you disposed of it. That would be a smart move. If, that is, there was some reason to do so.'

She didn't say anything.

'So you chased Rudy Caliente. Where did you go?'

'I followed him a couple blocks and lost him.'

'Where specifically?'

'I don't know — up Corning a ways, over Lawson or Parker or one of those. He was like a bat out of hell. I finally turned around and went back to the bar.'

'You caught up with him, is what I'm thinking. You took a potshot or two at him, didn't you?'

Anita said nothing.

'In a building at San Mateo and Parker, there's a bullet in the wall. I'm guessing it's a nine millimeter. And that the shell casings we found there will look a lot like the one I tracked down on the street in front of Saint Expedito.'

Anita shook her head, still looking down. 'I missed the SOB.'

'Come again?'

'Pulled up right next to him at a light and had him in my sights. He had his arm out the window and he wasn't paying attention. I'm a lousy shot. Missed him twice. He floored it and that was that. I turned around and came back.'

'Did you really dump the gun?'

She looked up at Frank and didn't reply.

'What were you worried about, Anita? Why not just tell me?'

'Tell you what — that I raced through the streets firing a weapon? A few laws being broken there, Detective? Stuff that could jeopardize my license?'

Frank stood up. She had broken more

laws than she might actually realize. Maybe. 'Thanks for the coffee, Anita. I think you better call your lawyer.'

He hated having to take out the handcuffs. He debated if they were really necessary.

11

Several separate items had appeared on different pages of the morning newspaper over a few days — for those who still read the actual newspaper.

One story noted in brief that three partially decomposed bodies had been found in a landfill in a small township about a hundred miles to the north. Authorities stated that there were as yet no identifications of the bodies but that fingerprints or dental records should ultimately reveal who they were.

A second item accounted that one Sergio Pacelli, manager of a local bar and dance club, had been reported missing by his wife. Five days previous, he had presumably gone to work as usual, but she later discovered that he had apparently packed bags and driven out of town without leaving any notification of his whereabouts. She had found his cell phone left behind in their bedroom. He had not returned nor contacted her since.

A third story concerned an investigation that had been opened into the reported disappearance of Vanessa Wilde, wife of local businessman William Wilde. Members of Vanessa's family had filed statements following inquiries and interviews by Police Detective Frank Vandegraf.

According to a fourth article, several civil cases involving the digital firm Prophet DKM had been settled privately and abruptly. Cases pending against the late Albert Landreaux, a.k.a. Al Land, had been summarily dismissed due to the death of the defendant.

A regular 'police blotter' feature noted that various indictments had been returned against three defendants — Gerald Lombard, Randall Joe Harkins Junior, and Amanda Darcy — for transportation of stolen goods across state lines, conspiracy to smuggle, possession of stolen property, and numerous other charges.

Only a few people actually noticed, much less read, all these items, and fewer had made any connection among all of them. One of those few was Detective Jilly Garvey.

★　★　★

The events were all still swirling in her head as she and Dan made their way across the squad room to the desk where Frank Vandegraf sat re-familiarizing himself with an older case file that was still open.

Jilly tossed a manila folder onto Frank's desk. A few sheets popped out just a bit with the impact.

'Only took a year and a day for ballistics to come back. Thank you kindly, Mister Morgan.' She cast a sideways glance at Dan.

Dan pulled and scanned a few sheets. 'Oh come on, Jilly, it was only a couple of weeks.'

'And?' Frank asked.

'You lucky sonofagun,' Dan muttered, shaking his head.

'The .38 slugs that killed Marina Belize and Ricky Wright were from Rudy Caliente's gun. Also the slug in Nick Lowell's car door . . . Rudy's.'

'Lucky sonofagun,' Dan interjected, pointing at Frank.

187

'Too bad we couldn't get Al's Glock. The street lady was killed with a 9mm and it's gotta be from Anita.'

Frank scratched his ear. 'But Anita's lawyer struck a deal and she's been talking. We might sew this one up yet.'

'The part I can't get my head around,' Dan said, 'is why Rudy shot Marina and her boyfriend.'

Frank shook his head. 'He was all messed up, Dan. He had been drinking and, who knows, maybe also something else entirely. He was distraught. His world was coming apart at the seams. He knew that his wife, who was the most important part of his entire world, was seeing some hot-shot flashy guy with more money than him. He couldn't stand to lose her.

'He saw her get into Nick Lowell's nice ride, nicer than any ride he'd ever have, and he snapped. The rest of the evening, he hardly showed great judgment, would you say?'

'I would not,' said Jilly.

'He's driving around, downing beer and vodka, getting angrier and less rational, he sees Nick's car parked in front of Saint Expedito, figures they're in the bar.

'He double-parks in front of the SUV to block it just in case, and goes in. Al Land is a flashy guy about the same size as his guy, sitting at a table with two glasses. Rudy puts two and two together and gets five and plugs him.

'Anita comes tearing out of the loo, grabs Al's gun and chases after Rudy. She takes a shot as he accelerates away and misses, and decides to pursue him in her own car. Funny thing is, they're only seconds ahead of the valet who's come for Nick's car and sees this scene go down.

'Anita chases Rudy down the street in their Lexus, catches up to him at a stoplight, pulls up to his left, rolls down her power windows, and squeezes off a couple shots at him. We've already established she can't shoot worth beans, she misses him but breaks his right-side window and, not knowing it, plugs the street lady.'

'Mary,' said Jilly. 'We've been calling her Mary. Mary X.'

'We still don't know her real name,'

Dan added. 'Nobody's ever come forward. Sad.'

Frank considered how he had come to the conclusion that they all had to count equally and hoped that one day someone would come forward looking for her. Then he resumed the timeline.

'Rudy's spooked and takes off and Anita turns back, but now Rudy gets indignant as well as scared, and decides he's going after *her*. He's so distraught all he can remember is that she's a sort of long-haired blonde in a silver sedan. Only a few blocks away, what does he see but . . . '

' . . . blonde Marina Belize in a grey Acura,' Jilly said. 'A bit of a stretch. With Ricky Wright in the car too.'

'I don't know, maybe he doesn't see Ricky. He figures this is the crazy dame that dared shoot at him so he drives by and takes a couple shots at her from the driver's side. Ricky, at the first sign of danger, brave and gallant soul he is, tries to escape out of the car and gets it in the back.'

'At least,' Jilly interjected, 'now Jané knows the cartel was *not* after Marina and isn't after her. Her new identity is safe and probably has been for some time now. Not enough to make up for losing her sister, I'm afraid — or learning that her father is truly dead.'

Dan returned to the timeline. 'And even after that, Rudy's night still isn't over. He apparently encounters Nick and Tia again and starts realizing he's made a big *big* mistake.'

'Gotta be,' Frank said. 'Tia tells Nick she needs to make a stop for, well, necessities, and he drops her off. Maybe he's going to park. He passes Rudy in the process.'

'That's when Rudy empties the last shot out of his .38 and hits the side of Nick's car,' Jilly said. 'Nick's no hero either and he floors it, heads for the hills.'

'Let's give him a break,' Dan added. 'He's never seen Rudy. Maybe he's got no idea that Rudy is after Tia. Whatever this guy with the gun has in mind, Nick figures he'll just get out of there before Tia can come back out. Maybe he's actually trying to protect Tia, lead Rudy away.'

'Gallant soul,' said Frank with a shake of his head. 'Whatever. Rudy sees Tia coming out of the store. He steps on the brakes. He's emptied his gun and doesn't have time to reload yet. But he's got his fishing and hunting knife in the glove compartment. He grabs it and goes after her.'

'We're still waiting on those blood results,' Dan said. 'What a surprise. But do any of us doubt that Rudy's knife and Tia's wound and blood are going to be a match?'

'Now Rudy's really in a panic,' Jilly jumped in, getting into the story. 'Not that up to now he's been a picture of clarity, mind you. He grabs her wallet and cell phone, maybe to make it look like a robbery, maybe whatever. He beats it out of there before he can be ID'd.

'Luckily for him he's in a neighborhood where nobody cares, certainly not the slacker store clerk. It's a wonder that some anonymous citizen ran in to call in the body. Anyway, Rudy knows he has to track down Nick.

'He reloads his gun, maybe finishes off the rest of his drinks, and trawls around the neighborhood, searching. He doesn't have far to go.'

Frank reclaimed the narrative. 'Nick has pulled into the Ready Rite parking lot, which is maybe the first place he feels safe to stop. He's getting out of his car and is frantically trying to call Tia. There's a brawl breaking out in the lot. Maybe that's what gets Rudy's attention. He pulls into the lot, sees Nick, recognizes him, grabs his gun, gets out of the car and walks up and plugs Nick while he's distracted trying to call Tia.'

'Meanwhile Luther Newcombe has just unintentionally killed Sonny Foster and is terrified in his own right,' Jilly said. 'In his hysteria to get away he jumps in *his* car, guns it, and . . . '

'Bang,' said Dan, smacking a fist into a palm. 'He ties the whole package up for us.'

'Question is,' asked Jilly, 'did his taking out Rudy make it easier in the end — or harder?'

'It just seemed too pat and easy for me from the git-go,' said Frank. 'It was like something that would happen in a book or a TV show, not in real life. Those other guys — Wilde, Scudder, the DKM bunch

193

— weren't quite right to me but somehow they seemed more logical.

'I wasn't ready to write Rudy's death off as an accident. Guy kills a perfect stranger with lots of enemies and gets taken out in a weird hit-and-run. If Luther's family hadn't made him come forward when they did, I'd still be spinning my wheels on that one.'

'Hard-luck guy, Rudy Caliente,' mused Dan. 'Bad day all around for him.'

'Yeah,' agreed Jilly. 'Hard luck. He wasn't a bad guy, it would seem. Nobody even thought he was capable of violence. The Rudy that acted out that night — he was like an alien. He spun out and snapped. Talk about looking down into an abyss. Before he could come back, he took them all down with him. It could have all gone down differently. Too bad. Way too bad.'

That seemed to be a sobering thought for them all. It ceased to be an intellectual puzzle they had unraveled and became the real-life catastrophe that had destroyed so many lives.

Dan broke the silence. 'Bad luck

seemed to come in eights this time.'

'*Achtmusik*,' muttered Frank.

'Please,' Dan said. 'Do *not* start that one again.'

'For once,' Jilly muttered, 'I totally agree with my partner there.'

A momentary attempt at awkward laughter quickly subsided and they collectively grew silent.

The squad room around them continued to buzz with activity. The trio had cleared their most recent load but there was no respite in sight for any of them.

Frank sat glumly in silence for a few beats before observing, 'And I assume you got the word from the captain this morning, that we are officially no longer authorized for overtime? Oh . . . and he congratulated me on clearing the murders, pending corroboration by the hard evidence. I assume he's told you the same.'

Dan nodded. 'Yeah, we got the same speech.'

'Did he also 'encourage' you to apply the same magnificent effort to clearing your other cases?'

195

Frank made a theatrical flourish at the stacked folders on his desk while twisting his face a bit.

'Thanks for saving my daughter from drowning,' Jilly recited, quoting the punchline to an all-too familiar joke. 'Now, where's her hat?'

'Par for the course,' said Frank. He looked at his watch, as if to say, the hell with it. 'Lunch? Free of guilt?'

Dan nodded. 'Are you treating, Mr. Know-it-all?'

'You mean, out of the magnificent bonus I will be earning for my crackerjack detection and deduction skills? Sure, why not.'

He said it without a smile as he rose from his desk and reached for his sport coat on the chair back. 'Pastrami sound good?'

They filed out of the squad room, three tired and hungry souls, wearily attempting half-hearted banter but none of them smiling.

The rush of exhilaration from the solved cases had been short-lived and was being quickly replaced by the realization of what exactly they had solved.

Jilly couldn't help but reflect on the crazy eight they now were sure they had cleared. She was no stranger to meaningless crimes but these seemed particularly senseless.

You want to find the bad guys, she mused. You want to speak for the deceased and avenge the wrongs against them. At least that was the idealized version of their job.

There was certainly no shortage of bad ones encountered in this case: drug cartels, crooked investigators, armed robbers, racketeers, street hustlers, ruthless and deceitful businessmen.

But they were all innocent. That was the sad irony. This was an irrational tragedy, set into motion and played out in a few short hours, without any set-in-stone villains.

So much waste, so little closure for so many.

Yes, these things actually could still bother her, and sometimes deeply. The night music hadn't totally become routine yet. Holding on to her humanity had its cost, she thought, but it was a necessary cost.

They were already on the street when her phone started playing Mozart once again. The music wasn't going to stop just yet.

THE END

THE SILVER HORSESHOE

Gerald Verner

John Arbinger receives an anonymous note — offering 'protection' from criminal gangs in exchange for £5,000 — with the impression of a tiny silver horseshoe in the bottom right-hand corner. Ignoring the author's warning about going to the police, Arbinger seeks the help of Superintendent Budd of Scotland Yard. But Budd is too late to save Arbinger from the deadly consequences of his actions, and soon the activities of the Silver Horseshoe threaten the public at large — as well as the lives of Budd and his stalwart companions . . .

A MURDER MOST MACABRE

Edmund Glasby

Jeremy Lavelle, leader of the esoteric Egyptian Society the Order of the True Sphinx, has illegally purchased an ancient Egyptian mummy. Watched by his enthralled followers, he opens the coffin and begins to unwrap the body . . . The head is that of an ancient scribe, his shrivelled and desiccated face staring eyelessly up from his coffin — yet from the neck down, wrapped up in layers of bandages, are not the mummified remains which they had expected. Instead, they stare in horror at the decapitated corpse of a recently killed man!

NEMESIS

Norman Firth

A burlesque beauty's fierce yearning
for vengeance is triggered following
the callous shooting of her younger
sister in a gang war. Rita's single-
handed efforts to avenge her sister's
death bring her into contact with some
of gangland's most ruthless killers, whose
animal instincts cause them to treat life
cheaply, and women callously. Through
many dangers Rita pursues her determined way towards the clearing of the
mystery surrounding her sister's slay-
ing, and the vengeance which has set
her whole being aflame . . .